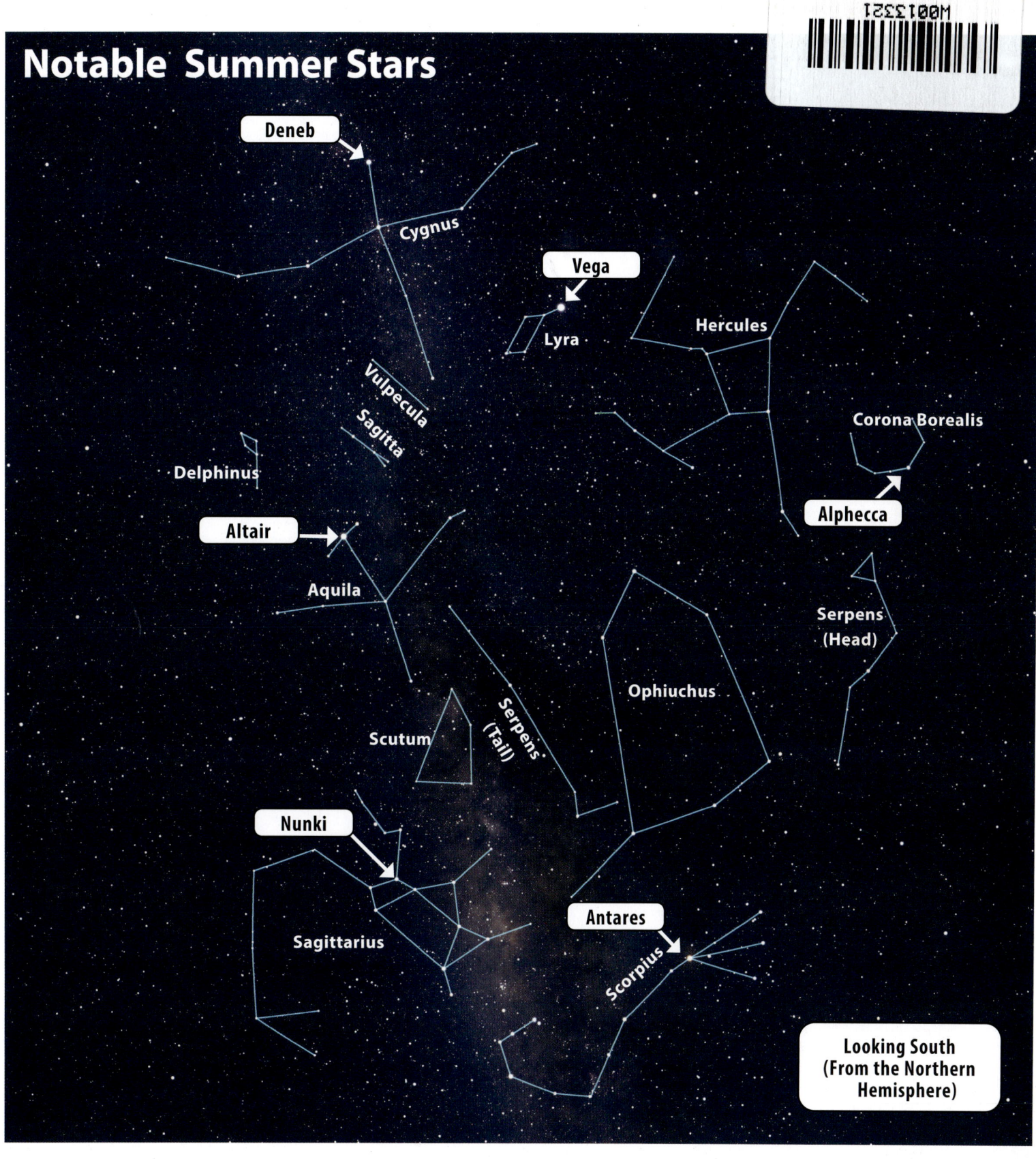

8. The Summer Beehive (IC 4665)

The Summer Beehive is also known as the "Hi" cluster, as it appears to spell the word in its star pattern. Early in the summer, the "original" Beehive Cluster may still be visible in the center of the springtime constellation, Cancer.

Ophiuchus lies in the direction of our galaxy's halo, a region of the sky filled with globular star clusters such as M10 and M12. Most of the globular star clusters are quite distant and small, but in the darkest skies, a keen observer may be able to pick out several of these clusters in binoculars. With astronomy binoculars and a tripod, and dark skies, this part of the sky becomes a very busy place.

OBSERVING LOG

Date: Time: Location:

Sky Conditions (Seeing/Transparency):

Instrument (Magnification/Aperture):

Notes:

Object of Interest: Summer Beehive (IC 4665)
Dark Sky Requirement: City Viewable
Object Type: Open Cluster
Brightness: 4
Distance: 1,100 Light-Years
Apparent Size: 70 Arc Minutes

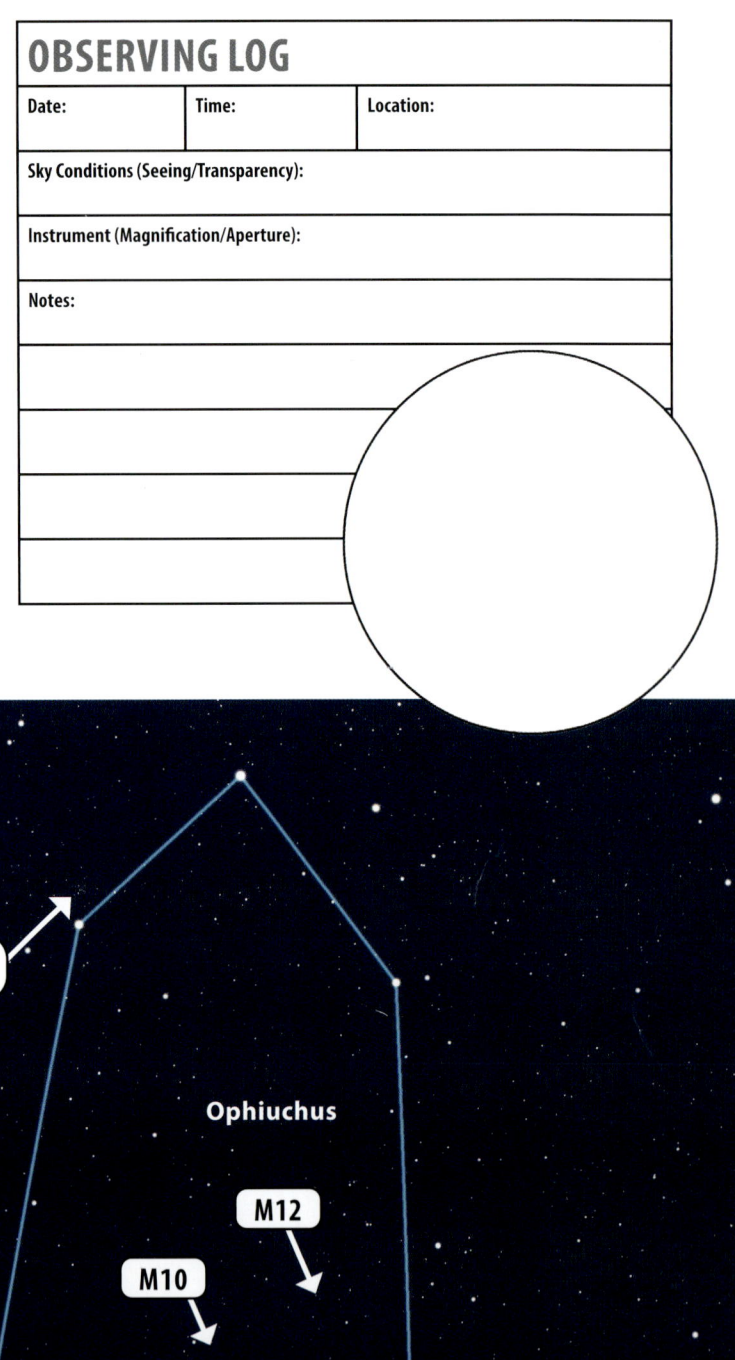

Image: Askar 180, 294MC, 1 min Kejimkujik, August 11, 2023

SUMMER

9. Tweedledee and Tweedledum Clusters

Two clusters, officially named NGC 6633 and IC 4756, form the binocular target known as the "Tweedledee and Tweedledum Clusters." For those who didn't know (like me), Tweedledee and Tweedledum are characters in a nursery rhyme and in the sequel to the book *Alice in Wonderland*.

The clusters are found about halfway between Aquila and Ophiuchus and, in dark skies, can be observed without binoculars. Although both of these clusters are about the same magnitude in brightness, NGC 6633 appears brighter and more compact, whereas the starlight in IC 4756 is less pronounced yet covers a larger area.

OBSERVING LOG

Date: | Time: | Location:

Sky Conditions (Seeing/Transparency):

Instrument (Magnification/Aperture):

Notes:

Object of Interest: NGC 6633 (Tweedledum)
Dark Sky Requirement: Suburbs
Object Type: Open Cluster
Brightness: 4.6
Distance: 1,200 Light-Years
Apparent Size: 20 Arc Minutes

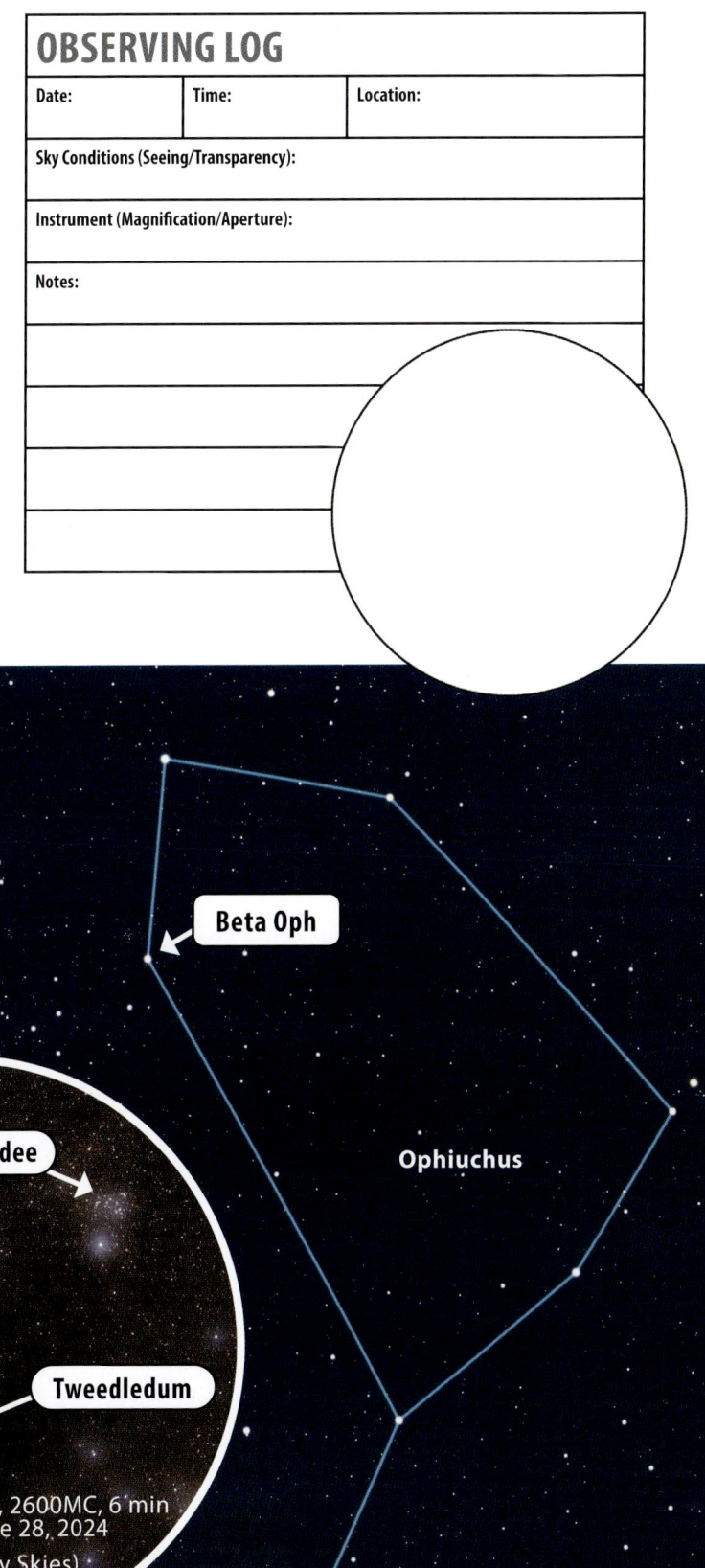

Image: Askar FMA180, 2600MC, 6 min Stargaze NS, June 28, 2024 (Through Hazy Skies)

SUMMER

10. The Antares Cluster and M4

The bright star Antares is part of an open cluster that has been given the designation Collinder 302. With binoculars, the globular cluster M4 appears within this open cluster. In reality, the globular cluster is thousands of times farther away. M4 is one of the brightest globular clusters in the summer sky.

In images like the one in the beginning of this section, Antares is surrounded by nebulae. However, in binoculars, it's hard to say if you're really seeing any nebulosity. That said, Antares does seem to have a certain glow about it, which could be due to the surrounding gas.

From the reasonably dark skies, M4 is very easy to find, primarily due to its proximity to Antares.

OBSERVING LOG

Date: Time: Location:

Sky Conditions (Seeing/Transparency):

Instrument (Magnification/Aperture):

Notes:

Object of Interest: M4
Dark Sky Requirement: Suburbs
Object Type: Globular Cluster
Brightness: 5.6
Distance: 7,200 Light-Years
Apparent Size: 36 Arc Minutes

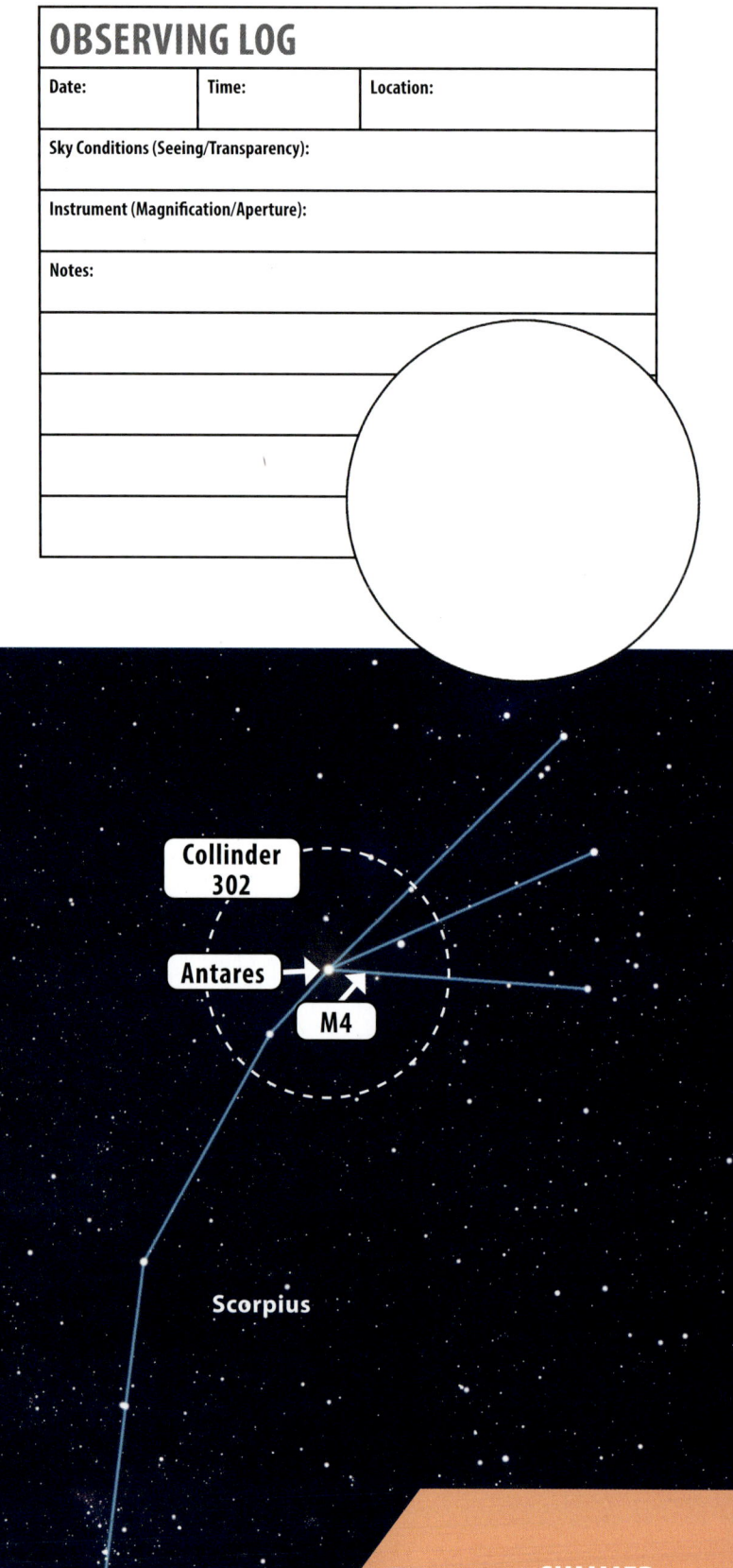

Image: Sharpstar 61, 294MC, 3 min
Stargaze NS, August 23, 2023

SUMMER

11. Great Sagittarius Cluster (M22)

M22 is often considered the most spectacular globular cluster in our sky, at least in the Northern Hemisphere. (The Southern Hemisphere has a much larger one called Omega Centauri.) The advantage M22 has over the slightly larger M13 is that this cluster is much easier to find. M22 is located just to the right of the bright star Kaus Borealis, the lid of the Teapot.

I don't have any trouble seeing or finding M22 without binoculars (or a telescope) from my observing site. Once you're familiar with this part of the sky, you simply point your binoculars at the top of the Teapot, and this cluster will quickly pop into view. If you're having trouble, look for a little triangular cluster of stars that almost looks like a Tesla Cybertruck; M22 is located right next to it.

OBSERVING LOG

Date: Time: Location:

Sky Conditions (Seeing/Transparency):

Instrument (Magnification/Aperture):

Notes:

Object of Interest: M22
Dark Sky Requirement: Suburbs
Object Type: Globular Cluster
Brightness: 5.1
Distance: 10,000 Light-Years
Apparent Size: 32 Arc Minutes

Image: Askar 180, 294MC, 5 min
Kejimkujik, August 11, 2023

SUMMER

12. Lagoon and Trifid (M8 and M20)

The Lagoon Nebula (M8) is by far the biggest and brightest binocular nebula visible in the summer sky from the Northern Hemisphere. When viewed from dark skies with the unaided eye, it appears as a tiny cloud hanging out over the Teapot asterism.

One of the challenges in taking the photo of this nebula for the book was that even a couple of minutes of exposure produced a bright and colorful image. I had to reduce the saturation and brightness quite a bit to get the image to appear as it did through binoculars from the same location.

If you look northwest of the Lagoon, you'll see the Trifid Nebula (M20) appear as a tiny smudge. Another small open cluster, Messier object Webb's Cross (M21), can also be resolved nearby.

OBSERVING LOG

Date: Time: Location:

Sky Conditions (Seeing/Transparency):

Instrument (Magnification/Aperture):

Notes:

Object of Interest: Lagoon Nebula (M8)
Dark Sky Requirement: Suburbs
Object Type: Star-Forming Nebula
Brightness: 6
Distance: 4,300 Light-Years
Apparent Size: 90 x 40 Arc Minutes

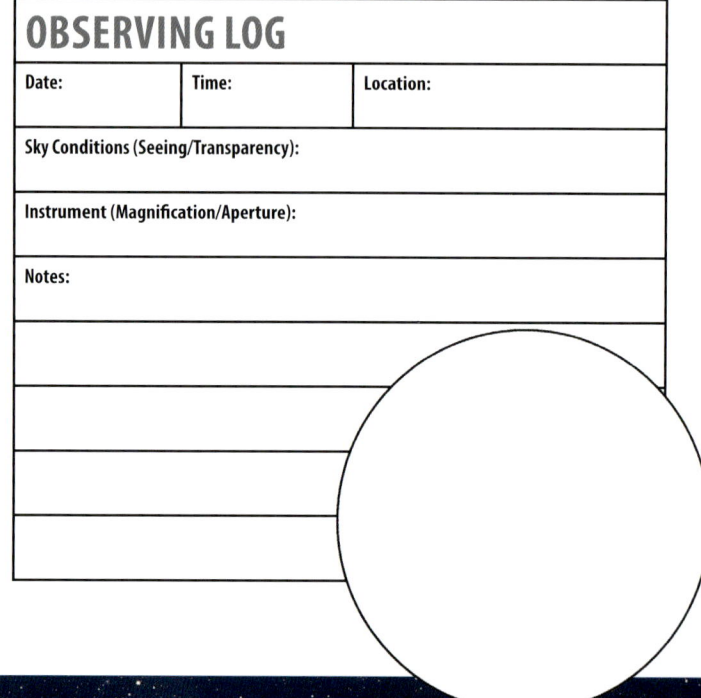

Image: Askar 180, 294MC, 6 min
Kejimkujik, August 11, 2023

SUMMER

13. Globular Cluster M13

M13 is considered to be the crown jewel of globular clusters, but there's an issue. In summer, M13 is almost directly overhead! If you're standing or sitting in a normal chair, you'll put a crick in your neck trying to view it. Hercules is also not a particularly bright constellation but is recognized primarily by the "keystone" asterism made of the four stars at its center. M13 is found between two of these stars. (For a much easier-to-view globular cluster, see M22.)

M13 is also one of the most impressive telescope targets. I had my 12-inch Dobsonian set up at a recent Dark Sky Event. I was using binoculars, and the person at the telescope kept saying, "Oh wow, oh wow" while viewing this target. Through binoculars, M13 appears as a big smudge. It's not an "Oh wow, that's beautiful," but more of an "Oh wow, I see something."

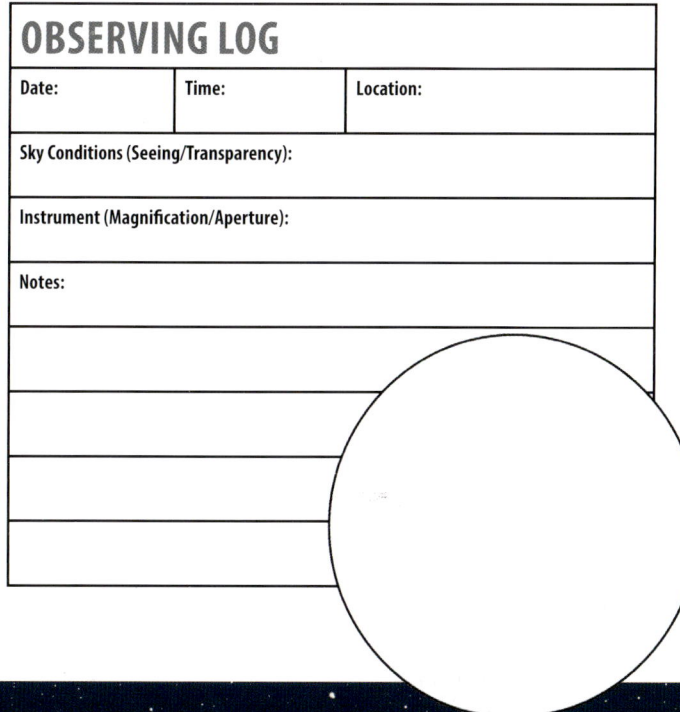

OBSERVING LOG
Date: Time: Location:
Sky Conditions (Seeing/Transparency):
Instrument (Magnification/Aperture):
Notes:

Object of Interest: M13 (Great Cluster in Hercules)
Dark Sky Requirement: Suburbs
Object Type: Globular Cluster
Brightness: 5.8
Distance: 23,000 Light-Years
Apparent Size: 20 Arc Minutes

Image: Askar 180, 2600MC, 6 min Tucson, May 9, 2024

SUMMER

14. The Sagittarius Star Clouds

The Small Sagittarius Star Cloud is actually a Messier object, M24, while the Large Sagittarius Star Cloud is simply one of the most dense patches of stars in our night sky.

I captured the image below from Kejimkujik National Park, and I did my best to edit it so that it closely resembles how the sky appeared through the binoculars on that night (as I've done with all the images in this book). As you can see, there are several other notable features within the wide binocular field of view. You can see M17, the Swan Nebula, as well as M18, a small open cluster.

The Large Sagittarius Star Cloud fills the space between M8, the Lagoon Nebula, one of the most impressive binocular nebulae, and Ptolemy's Cluster (M7), the bright (and large) star cluster between Sagittarius and Scorpius.

OBSERVING LOG

Date:	Time:	Location:

Sky Conditions (Seeing/Transparency):

Instrument (Magnification/Aperture):

Notes:

Image: Askar FMA180, 294MC, 6 min, Kejimkujik, August 11, 2023

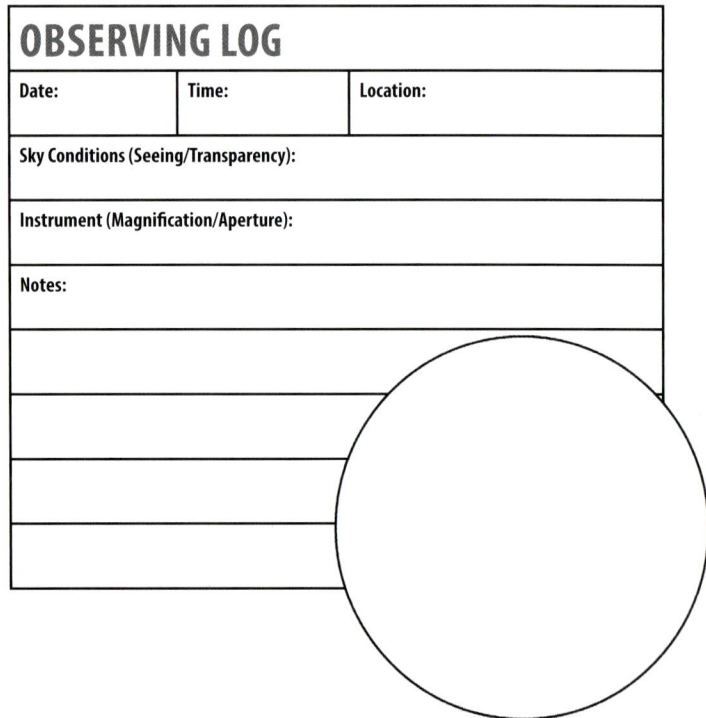

SUMMER

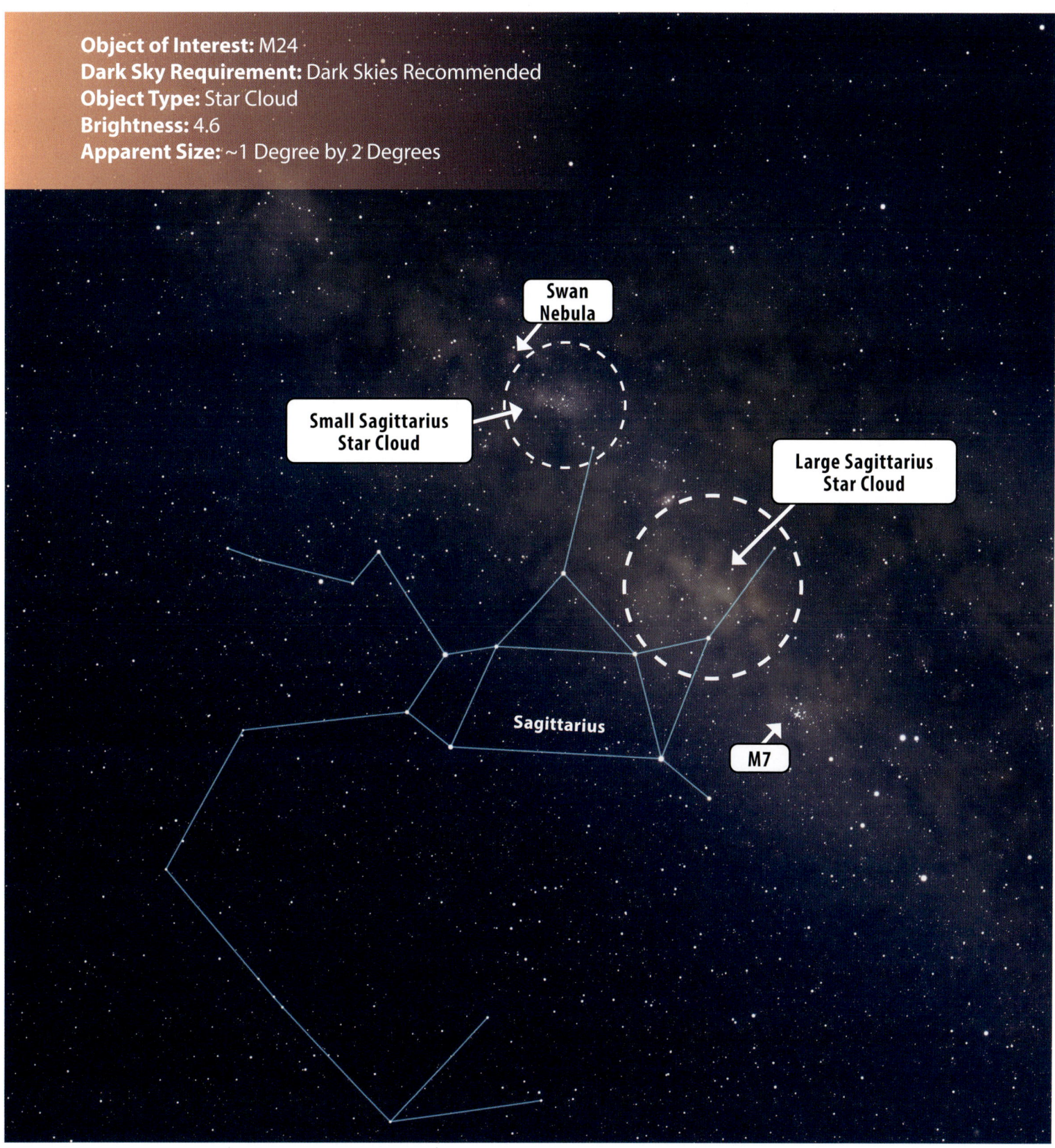

15. Coathanger (Brocchi's Cluster)

Along with the Andromeda Galaxy and Kemble's Cascade, the Coathanger is among the most popular binocular targets. This asterism of ten stars is just a little bit too big to fit into the field of view of most telescopes. Its stars, mostly 5th and 6th magnitude in brightness, are just out of visual range in most seeing conditions.

Finding the Coathanger in binoculars is fairly easy, assuming you can find Albireo with the naked eye. Simply pan the binoculars around Albireo, and you'll run into it. For a more direct approach, it can be found exactly halfway from Altair to Vega.

The spelling of the cluster is a particular mystery since Coathanger normally is two words but is one word in astronomy.

OBSERVING LOG

Date:
Time:
Location:
Sky Conditions (Seeing/Transparency):
Instrument (Magnification/Aperture):
Notes:

Object of Interest: The Coathanger
Dark Sky Requirement: Suburbs
Object Type: Open Cluster
Brightness: 3.4
Distance: 4,200 Light-Years
Apparent Size: 89 Arc Minutes

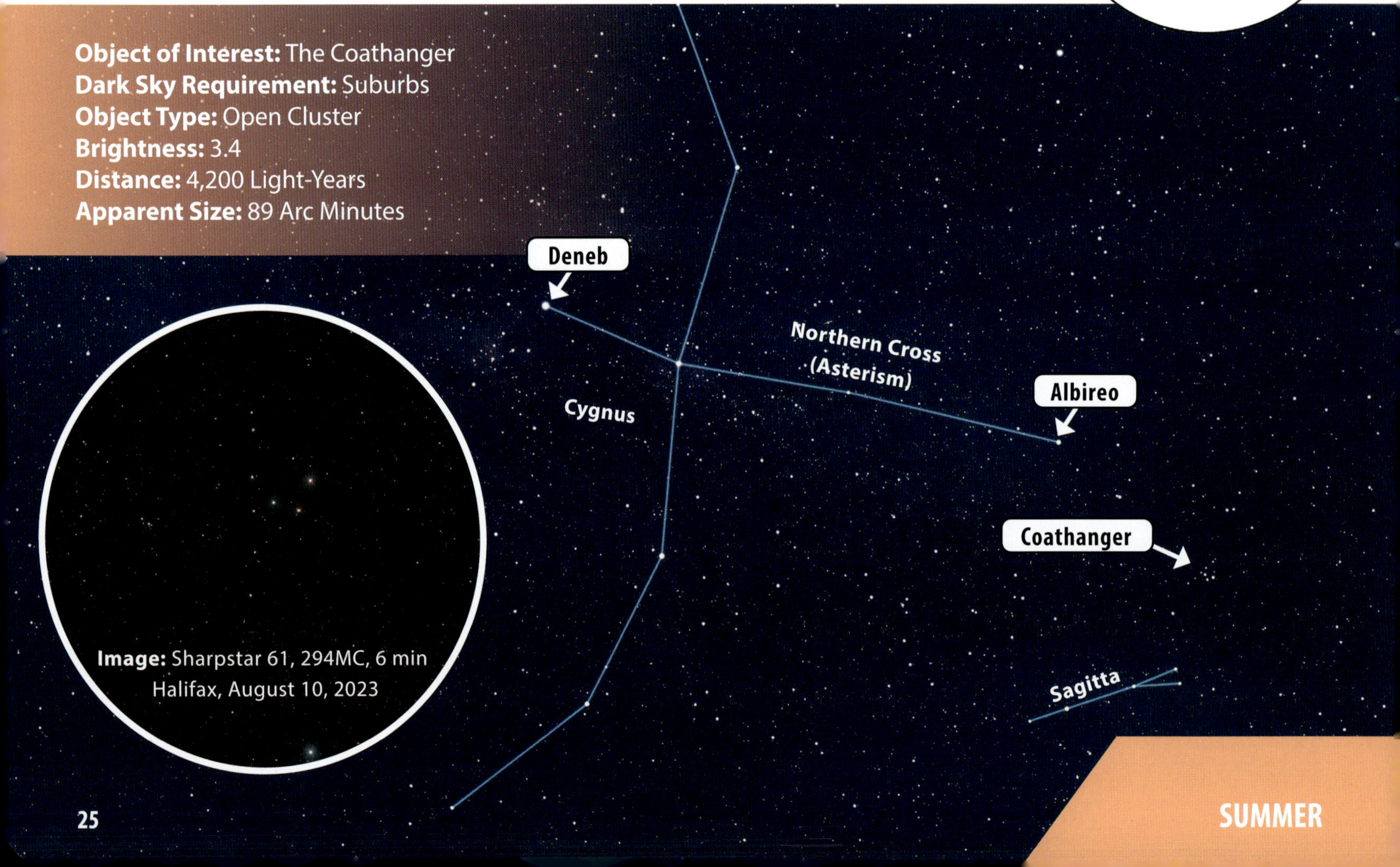

Image: Sharpstar 61, 294MC, 6 min Halifax, August 10, 2023

SUMMER

16. Hockey Stick (Omicron Cygni)

This was actually one of the very first, if not the first, astronomical targets I ever viewed through binoculars that made me say, "Wow, you know, that's really beautiful." All three stars can be seen with the naked eye, but through the binoculars, you really see the dynamics in the color. These three bright stars form the "Hockey Stick" asterism. Omicron 2 Cyg forms the top of the shaft, while Omicron 1 Cygni and 30 Cygni form the blade.

The most popular double star in the sky, Albireo, is nearby at the foot of the Northern Cross. With big astronomy binoculars and zoom binoculars, splitting Albireo is not too hard, but with regular binoculars, it's a bit of a challenge. Maybe we should call the Hockey Stick stars "binocular Albireo" as they share the contrasting colors but without the requirement of a telescope.

OBSERVING LOG

Date:　　　　Time:　　　　Location:

Sky Conditions (Seeing/Transparency):

Instrument (Magnification/Aperture):

Notes:

Object of Interest: Omicron 1 Cyg and 30 Cygni
Dark Sky Requirement: City Viewable
Object Type: Double Star (Visual)
Brightness: 3.8 and 4.8
Distance: 880 and 610 Light-Years
Separation: 5.5 Arc Minutes

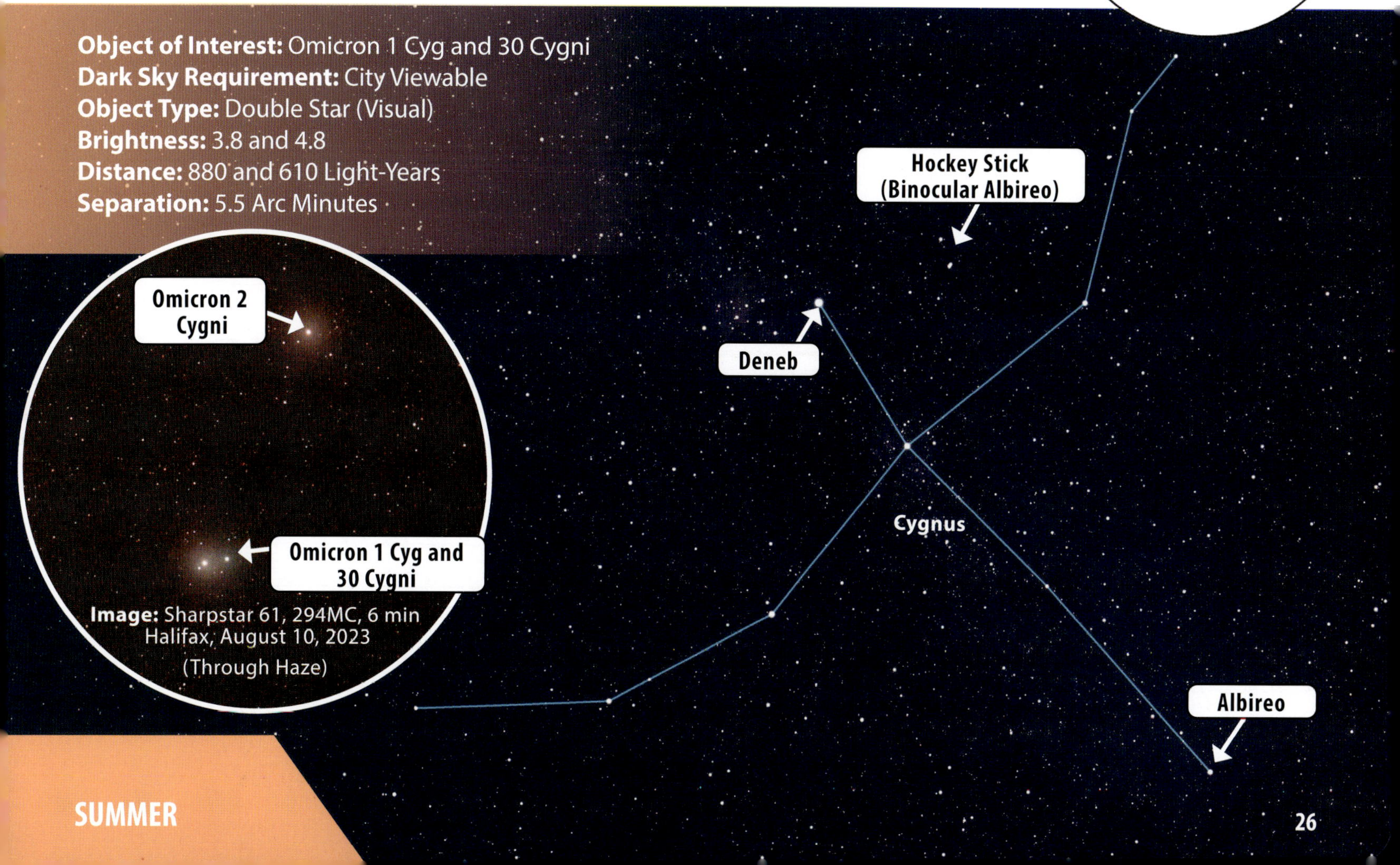

Omicron 2 Cygni

Omicron 1 Cyg and 30 Cygni

Image: Sharpstar 61, 294MC, 6 min
Halifax, August 10, 2023
(Through Haze)

Hockey Stick (Binocular Albireo)

Deneb

Cygnus

Albireo

SUMMER

26

17. The Dumbbell (M27)

This bright planetary nebula fills the field of view in my 12-inch Dobsonian telescope. It's the most popular planetary nebula in the sky, along with the Ring Nebula (M57). M57 is not officially a target in this book because of its small size. In binoculars, finding the Dumbbell Nebula is challenging, but rewarding nonetheless.

Unlike most planetary nebulae, which tend to look like, well, dim planets, this object looks more like an apple core than anything else (more so than a dumbbell, in my opinion).

The Dumbbell Nebula is technically within the boundaries of the constellation Vulpecula, though it is most easily found by searching above the Arrow (Sagitta).

OBSERVING LOG

Date: Time: Location:

Sky Conditions (Seeing/Transparency):

Instrument (Magnification/Aperture):

Notes:

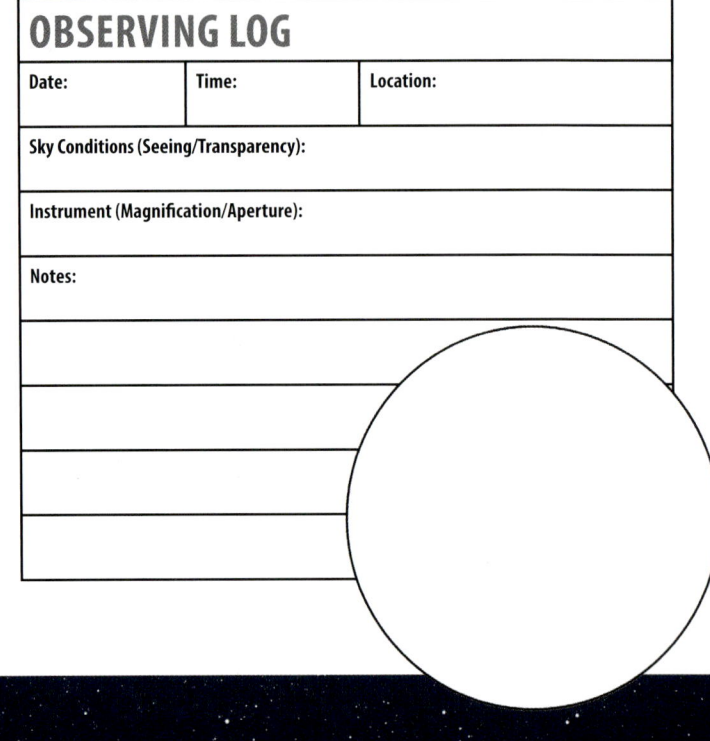

Object of Interest: M27
Dark Sky Requirement: Suburbs
Object Type: Planetary Nebula
Brightness: 7.1
Distance: 1,400 Light-Years
Apparent Size: 8 x 6 Arc Minutes

Image: Askar FMA180, 294MC, 6 min
Kejimkujik, August 11, 2023

SUMMER

18. Ptolemy's Cluster (M7)

For those at mid-Northern latitudes, this cluster barely makes its way over the horizon. Originally, I photographed most of the summer targets from Kejimkujik National Park, but this cluster was simply too low. I snagged it the following May from Biosphere 2 in Arizona. The image also contains a more compact binocular cluster, M6, which looks like a butterfly.

If you have a clear view of the southern horizon, M7 is quite easy to find. It lies right between the Teapot and Fishhook asterisms. The cluster itself really stands out in binoculars. The brightest stars seem to form an hourglass shape, with a tiny square-shaped gap in the middle. This cluster is also called Ptolemy's Cluster, named for the Roman astronomer who first recorded his observation over one thousand years prior to the invention of the telescope.

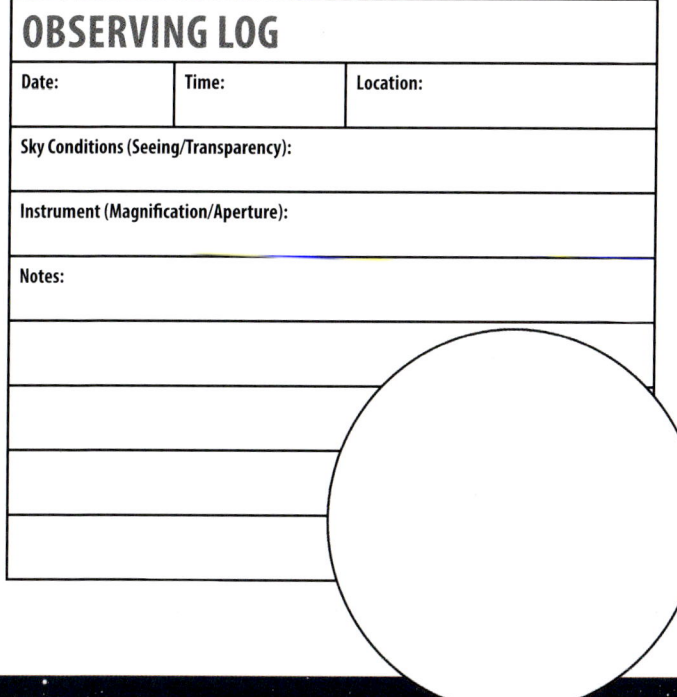

OBSERVING LOG

Date: Time: Location:

Sky Conditions (Seeing/Transparency):

Instrument (Magnification/Aperture):

Notes:

Object of Interest: Ptolemy's Cluster (M7)
Dark Sky Requirement: Suburbs
Object Type: Open Cluster
Brightness: 3.2
Distance: 980 Light-Years
Apparent Size: 80 Arc Minutes

Image: Askar 180, 2600MC, 3 min
Tucson, May 10, 2024

SUMMER

19. The Wild Duck Cluster (M11)

This cluster, M11, can be a challenge to find in a telescope due to its compact nature, but in binoculars, with a nice wide field, it jumps right out. Point the binoculars at the tail of the Eagle in the constellation Aquila, and you can't miss it. This cluster consists of about two dozen relatively bright stars.

M11 was originally named the Wild Duck Cluster by a British naval officer named William Henry Smyth for its resemblance to a flock of ducks in flight, but these days, I call it the "Borg Cube." (I did not come up with this; I read it somewhere on the Internet a long time ago.) At first glance, the cluster, through binoculars or a telescope, resembles a bright white cube, almost like a Borg Cube from *Star Trek* in the light of a star.

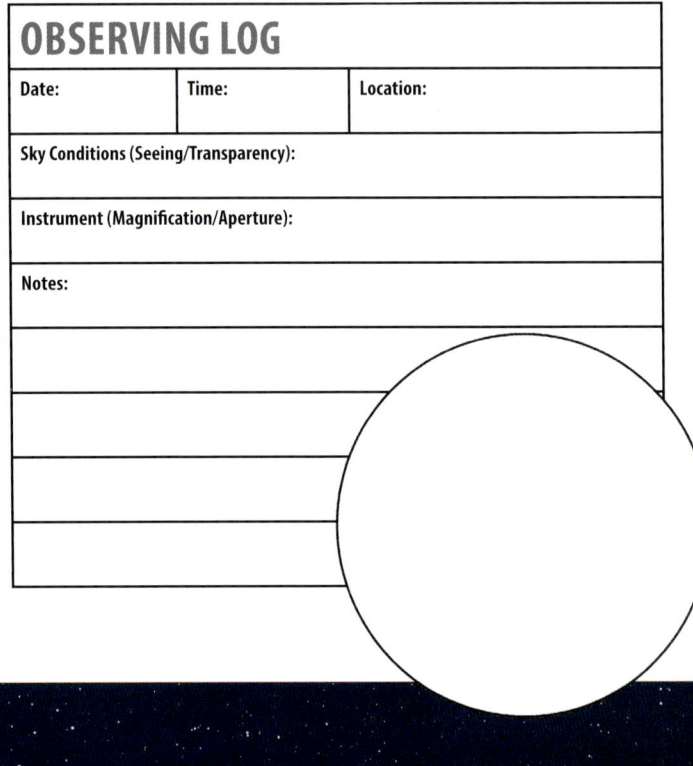

OBSERVING LOG

Date: Time: Location:

Sky Conditions (Seeing/Transparency):

Instrument (Magnification/Aperture):

Notes:

Object of Interest: M11
Dark Sky Requirement: Suburbs
Object Type: Open Cluster
Brightness: 5.8
Distance: 6,100 Light-Years
Apparent Size: 32 Arc Minutes

Image: Askar FMA180, 294MC, 6 min Kejimkujik, August 11, 2023

M11

SUMMER

20. The Scutum Star Cloud and M26

After observing M11, let your eyes adapt to the darkness inside your binoculars, lower your field of view, and enter the Scutum Star Cloud. This incredibly dense patch of the Milky Way is bisected by a "Dark Nebula." These dark patches, visible only in the darkest skies, have their own designations. If you're collecting Messier objects, open cluster M26 is located below the star cloud.

The nearest dark nebula to M11 is known as "Barnard 318" or simply B318, named by the American astronomer E. E. Barnard. Barnard is one of the only humans to actually have a star named after him (yes, those "Name a Star" websites are scams). Barnard's star is one of the closest stars to our solar system, yet only a 9th magnitude star located near the Summer Beehive.

OBSERVING LOG

Date: Time: Location:

Sky Conditions (Seeing/Transparency):

Instrument (Magnification/Aperture):

Notes:

Object of Interest: M26
Dark Sky Requirement: Suburbs
Object Type: Open Cluster
Brightness: 8.0
Distance: 5,400 Light-Years
Apparent Size: 7 Arc Minutes (Tiny)

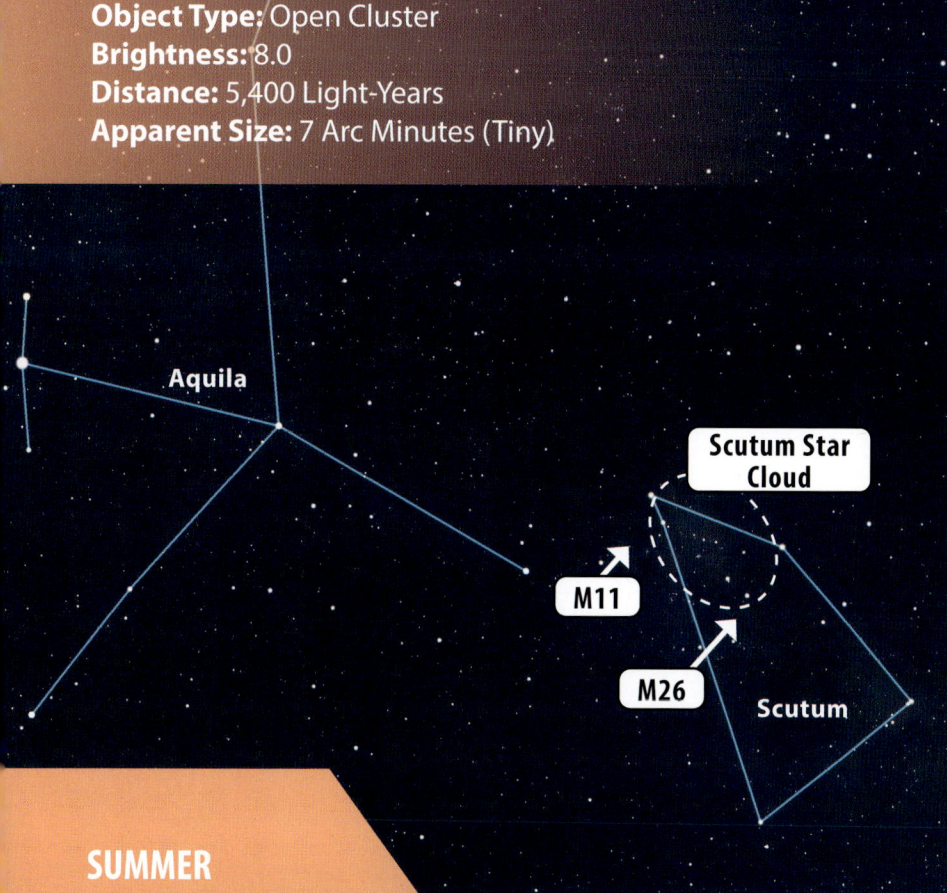

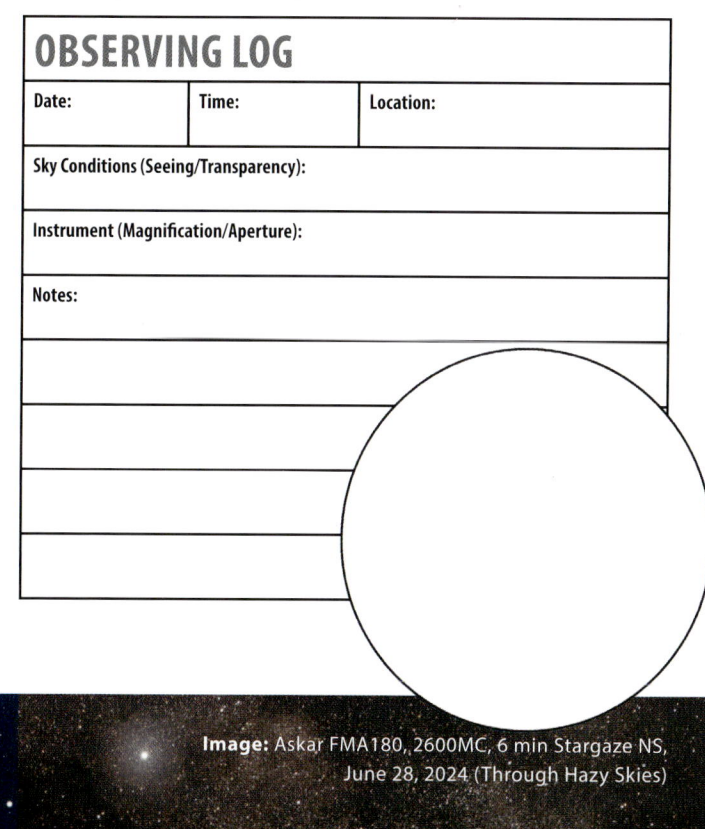

Image: Askar FMA180, 2600MC, 6 min Stargaze NS, June 28, 2024 (Through Hazy Skies)

SUMMER

AUTUMN TARGETS

The best thing about stargazing in autumn is that the nights are getting longer, and the summer targets are still visible in the evening sky. In fact, the Summer Triangle is visible until December! I went camping on October 15 this year, and with a low horizon, we still got a good view of the star clusters and nebulae surrounding the summer constellation Sagittarius as well. This is why autumn is my favorite stargazing season. Not only do you get most of the summer targets, and all of the autumn targets, but, with Cassiopeia high in the sky, some of the best circumpolar targets as well.

For the constellations specific to autumn, I use three prominent star patterns to navigate around the sky. The first is the Great Square in Pegasus. The second is the head of the whale in Cetus, and the third is the Circlet (which sort of looks like the head of the whale) in Pisces.

In light-polluted skies, when looking south, sometimes it appears that the autumn sky contains almost no stars at all! This is because Pisces, Cetus, Aquarius, and Capricornus contain no bright stars and tend to be quite low on a mid-northern hemisphere horizon. In this case, it's best to stargaze to the north, taking advantage of the rising clusters in Perseus and Cassiopeia.

This color image of the Andromeda Galaxy is a 2.5-hour exposure taken from the city. If you have perfectly good skies (like in the Arizona desert), the object will almost look this good in binoculars.

This is a long-exposure image. To see how the Andromeda Galaxy looks though binoculars, see page 37.

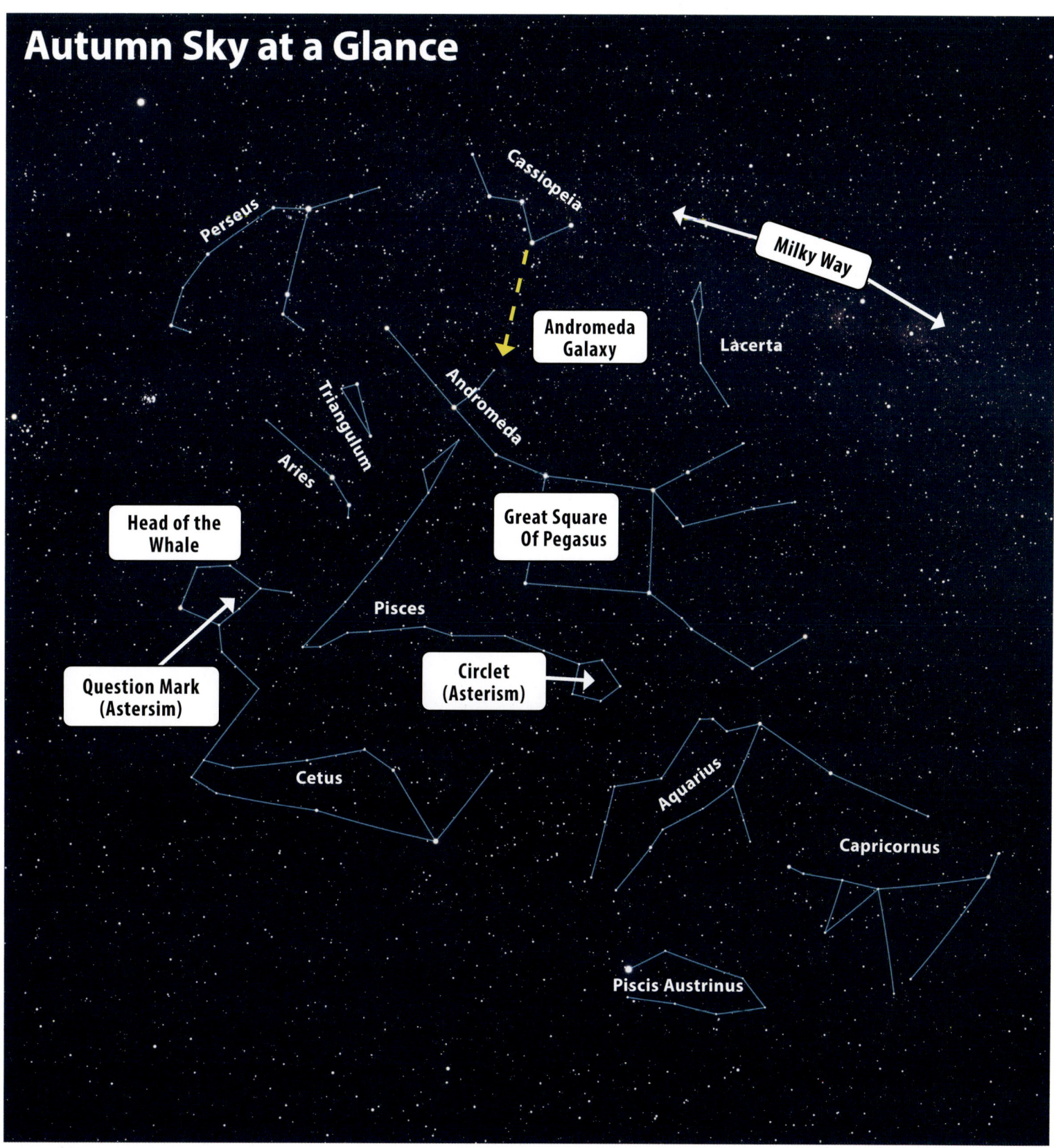

21. Notable Autumn Stars

Autumn's constellations contain fewer bright stars than the other seasons. This is perhaps because most of the constellations lie off the plane of the Milky Way. One star of note is Alpheratz, which connects the star lines of Andromeda and Pegasus. Alpheratz is technically located within Andromeda.

The star Algol is an eclipsing binary star that drops in brightness from 2.1 to 3.4 for ten hours once every two days. This occurs when the fainter pair in this multi-star system passes in front of its brighter sibling.

Mirfak is found at the center of one of the most beautiful clusters in the sky. Another star, Mirach, is helpful in locating the Andromeda Galaxy.

The star Fomalhaut is the brightest star in the autumn sky, however, for Northern Hemisphere observers it is often found very low on the southern horizon.

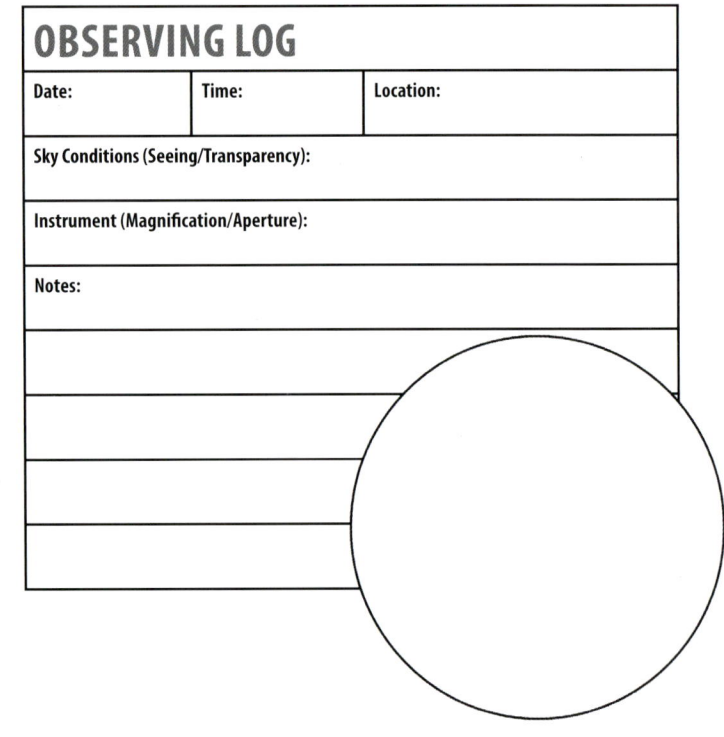

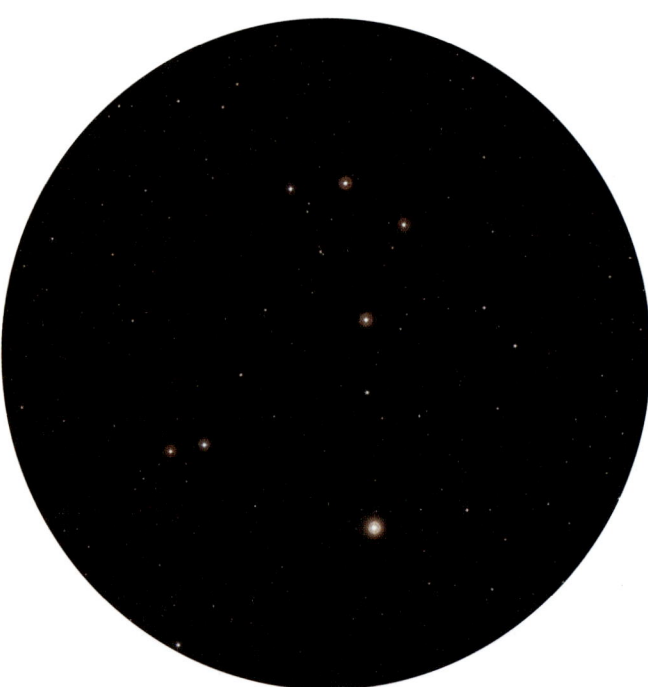

The image of the Question Mark asterism
Credit: DSS2

These pictures of Algol were taken by RASC astronomer Larry McNish on the nights of August 10 and 11 during the 2007 Saskatchewan Summer Star Party at Cypress Hills Saskatchewan in Canada.

In the top image, you can see that Algol is much brighter than the nearby red star (Rho Persei). However, in the bottom image, these same stars appear equally as bright.

OBSERVING LOG

Date: Time: Location:

Sky Conditions (Seeing/Transparency):

Instrument (Magnification/Aperture):

Notes:

AUTUMN

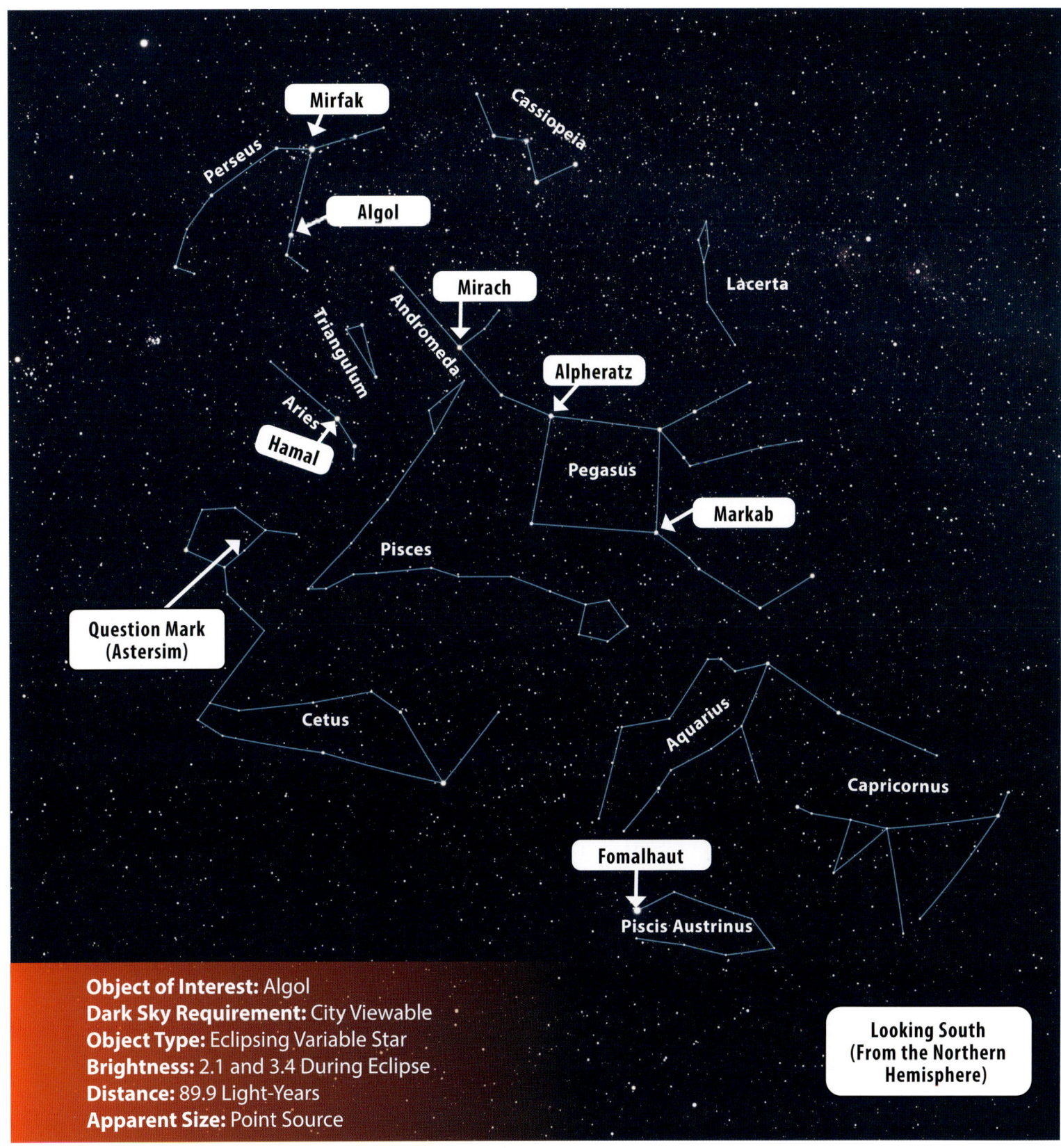

22. Fall Double Stars and Asterisms

Most of the double stars listed here are included in the Astronomical League's Binocular Double Star Observing Program. The program is most likely designed for those with tripod-mounted large-aperture astronomy binoculars, as most of their selected double stars are extremely challenging to split. For this book, I've tried to choose only the easiest (and prettiest) double stars from the list.

One of the biggest challenges in astronomy club observing programs is that their tables tend to list the names of objects with Greek lettering or unique abbreviations. Translating Greek so you can type a star name into astronomy software can be quite frustrating. With RASC, in particular, it's far more challenging to determine what star they're talking about than to actually find the star in the sky. This is why my books include a map for every target.

In researching for this book, I found an interesting website from the Milwaukee Astronomical Society, which notes several autumn asterisms that I'd not heard of before. These are always quite a lot of fun to try and find, and from this page I've included Frederick's Glory, a "modern" constellation that never made it onto the official list; the Question Mark, in the Head of the Whale; Home Plate Near Andromeda; and the Golf Putter near Triangulum (which includes the Double Star, 56 Andromeda).

OBSERVING LOG

Date: Time: Location:

Sky Conditions (Seeing/Transparency):

Instrument (Magnification/Aperture):

Notes:

Additional sketching circles are provided in the back of this book.

Image of the Home Plate asterism
Credit: DSS2

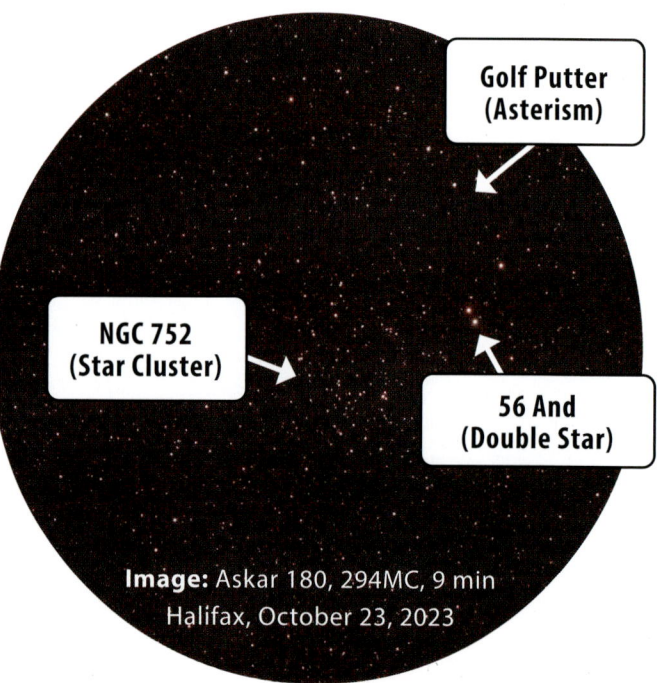

Image: Askar 180, 294MC, 9 min
Halifax, October 23, 2023

AUTUMN

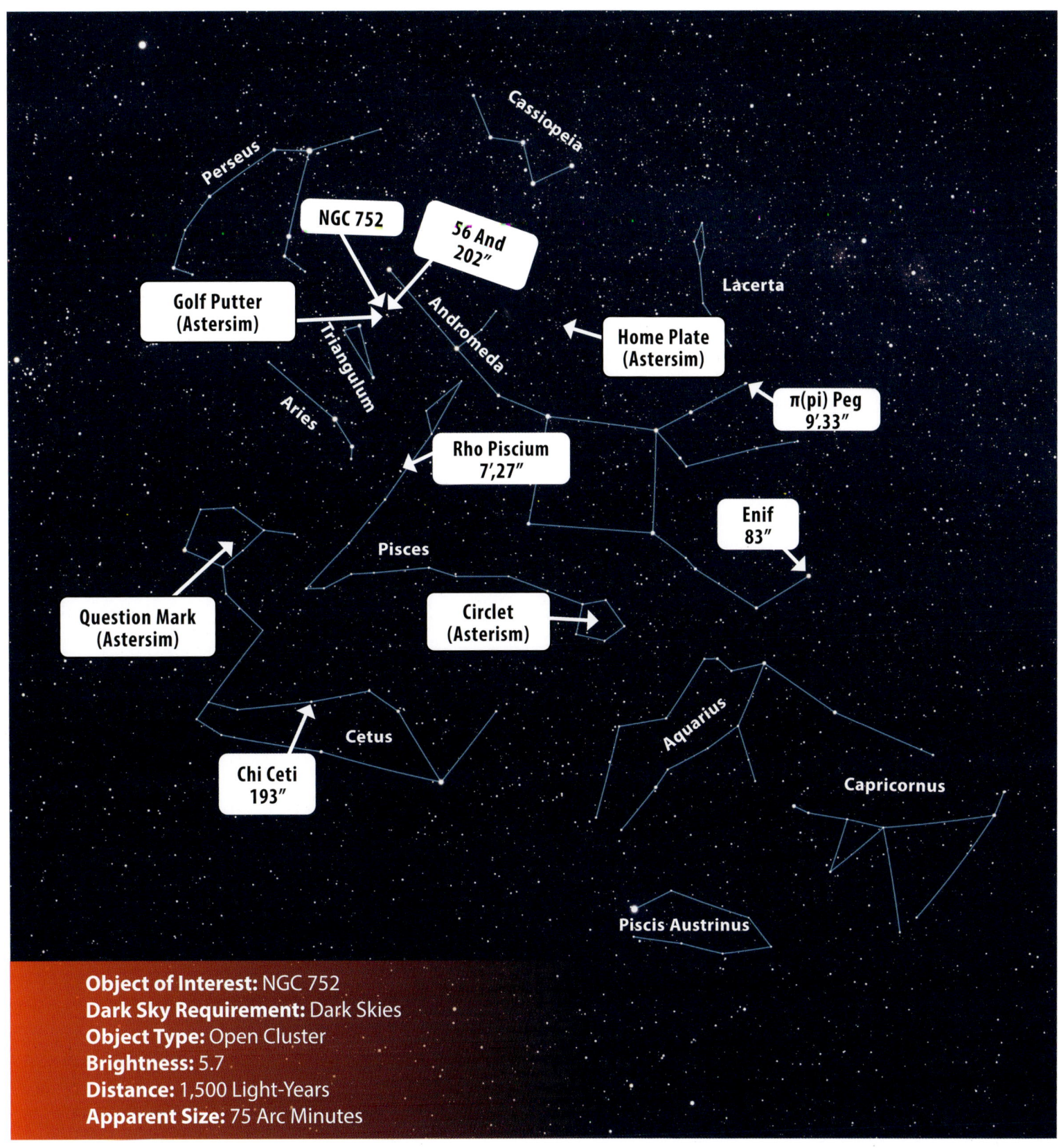

Object of Interest: NGC 752
Dark Sky Requirement: Dark Skies
Object Type: Open Cluster
Brightness: 5.7
Distance: 1,500 Light-Years
Apparent Size: 75 Arc Minutes

23. Andromeda Galaxy (M31)

If you plan on observing the Andromeda Galaxy, M31, don't even reach for your telescope. Binoculars are the only way to observe this galaxy in its full splendor. It took me a long time to train myself to see M31 without a telescope at all. Even from Hawaii, on top of the mountain, I had trouble picking it out (probably because I kept looking at my camera, not letting my eyes adapt to the dark).

Once I realized how much sky Andromeda occupies, I was able to train my eyes to look for a bright smudge in the sky, several times the size of the full Moon! I realized I had failed before because I was looking for something smaller, not something resembling a small cloud! Back in Nova Scotia, I observed M31 without any optics, then slowly brought the binoculars up to my face. The view was incredible. I spent quite some time that night observing every detail. It was simply that pretty.

OBSERVING LOG

Date: Time: Location:

Sky Conditions (Seeing/Transparency):

Instrument (Magnification/Aperture):

Notes:

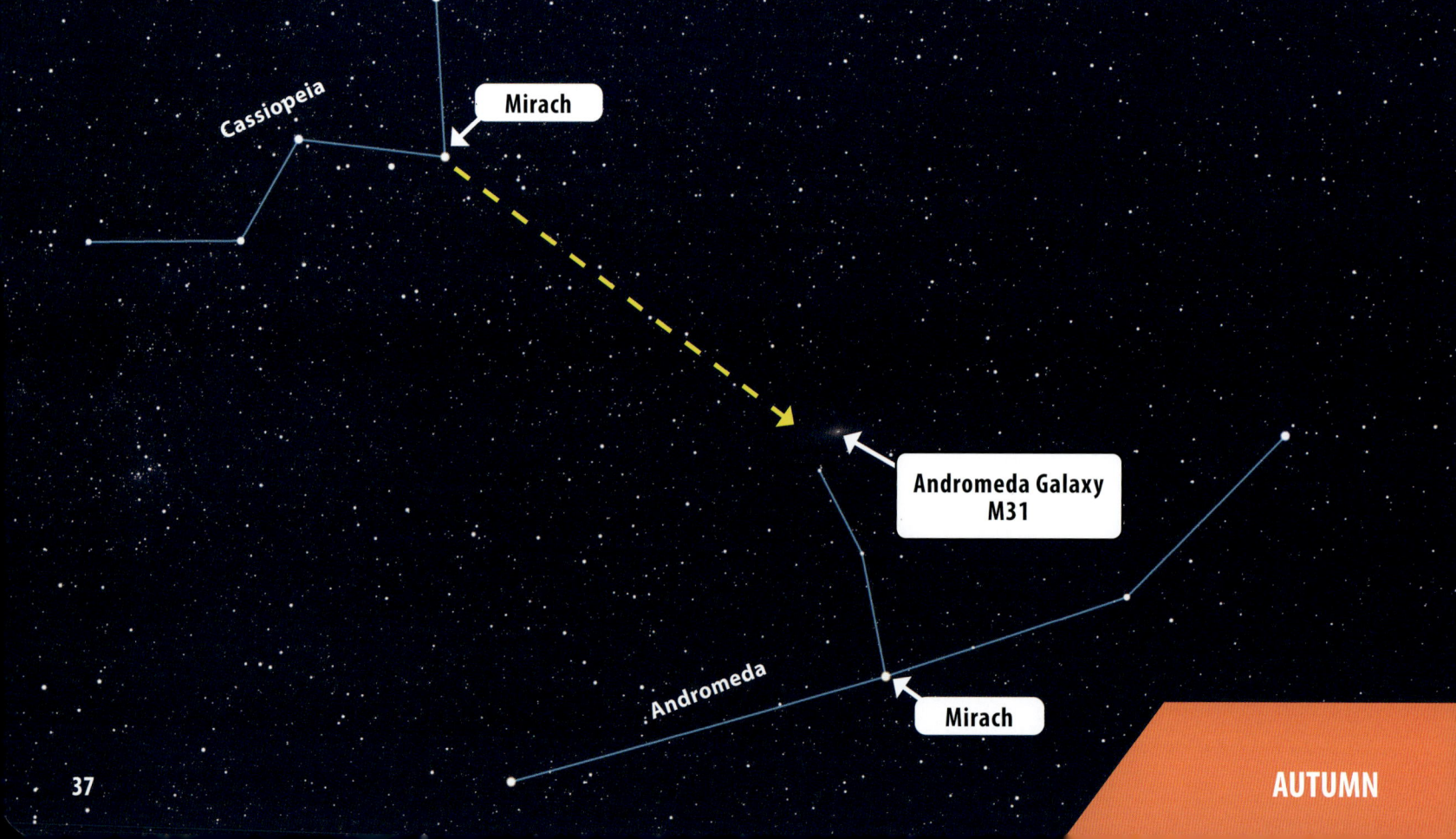

AUTUMN

Object of Interest: The Andromeda Galaxy
Dark Sky Requirement: Suburbs
Object Type: Spiral Galaxy
Brightness: 3.3
Distance: 2,500,000 Light-Years
Apparent Size: 178 x 70 Arc Minutes

Image: Askar 180, 294MC, 9 min, Kejimkujik, August 11, 2023

24. Triangulum Galaxy (M33)

Every year in Nova Scotia, Kejimkujik National Park and National Historic Site hosts its annual Dark Sky Weekend. In the summer of 2023, 250 campers milled around our group of perhaps a dozen or so volunteers, of which about half had brought telescopes.

By about midnight, it was just me and a few volunteers left. I sat down in a lawn chair, exhausted from the day's events. I first began admiring M31 in binoculars, and then binocular expert Tony Schellinck said, "You know, M33 is right above the treeline." I panned the binoculars toward the trees, and there it was! I was using zoom binoculars at about 15x. The galaxy took up about a quarter of the width of my binoculars' field of view! Of course, it still looked like a smudge, but you could clearly see that it wasn't round, and I could even begin to see some of the spiral structure.

OBSERVING LOG

Date: Time: Location:

Sky Conditions (Seeing/Transparency):

Instrument (Magnification/Aperture):

Notes:

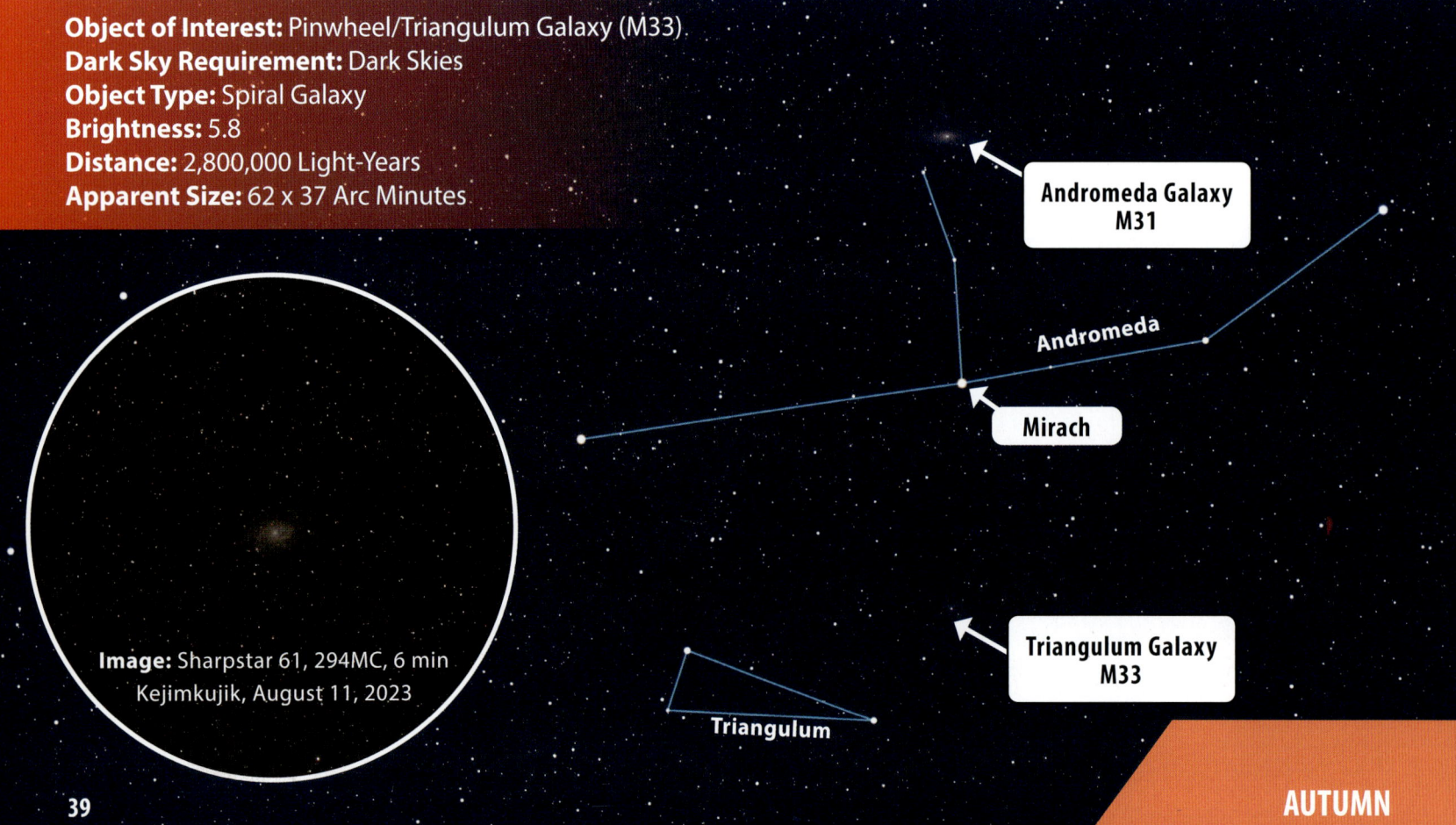

Object of Interest: Pinwheel/Triangulum Galaxy (M33)
Dark Sky Requirement: Dark Skies
Object Type: Spiral Galaxy
Brightness: 5.8
Distance: 2,800,000 Light-Years
Apparent Size: 62 x 37 Arc Minutes

Image: Sharpstar 61, 294MC, 6 min
Kejimkujik, August 11, 2023

25. The Pegasus Clusters (M15 and M2)

With M22 having dropped below the horizon, and M13 getting low in the sky in the west, a stargazer's focus will shift exclusively to the autumn sky, where two large globular clusters flank the head of Pegasus.

It's hard to picture this constellation as Pegasus (the winged horse) from the Northern Hemisphere, as it appears upside down. Three tendrils of stars extend from the western edge of the "Great Square," two of which represent the front legs. The third tendril is the head and neck.

M15 is found by following a line through the face of Pegasus, while M2 is found by following a line straight through the neck. These clusters won't appear as large as M22 or M13, but in an area of the sky vacant of bright stars, they'll appear as fuzzy stars in modestly dark skies.

OBSERVING LOG

Date: Time: Location:

Sky Conditions (Seeing/Transparency):

Instrument (Magnification/Aperture):

Notes:

Object of Interest: M2
Dark Sky Requirement: Dark Skies
Object Type: Globular Cluster
Brightness: 6.5
Distance: 38,000 Light-Years
Apparent Size: 16 Arc Minutes

M15
Image: Askcar 180, 294MC, 6 min
Kejimkujik, August 12, 2023

M2
Image: Askcar 180, 294MC, 9 min
Kejimkujik, August 12, 2023

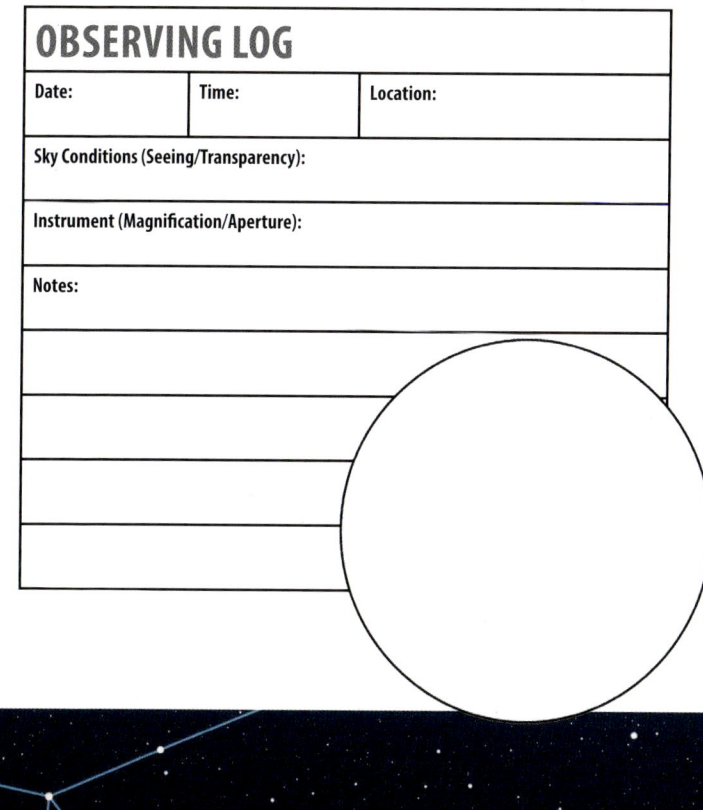

The Great Square of Pegasus

M15
Enif
Neck Head
M2
Saladsuud

AUTUMN

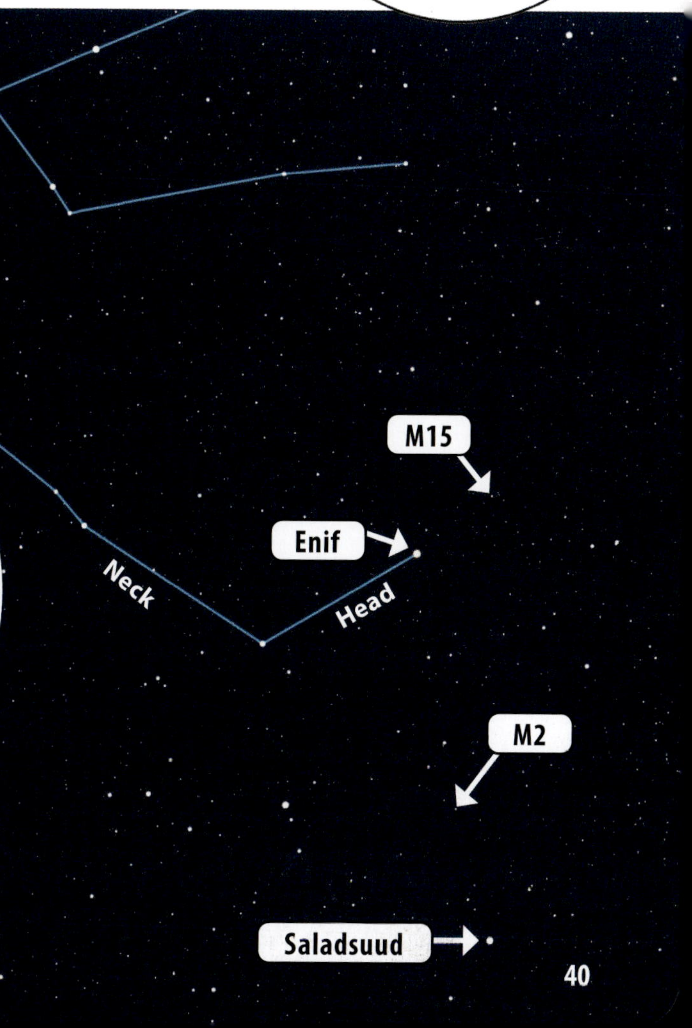

26. Alpha Persei Group and M34

An unappreciated treasure surrounds the bright star Mirfak. This wonderful collection contains an asterism that reminds Gary Seronik of a Canada goose. Perhaps that's why Stellarium has this asterism labeled as "The Christmas Goose." This asterism is technically part of the Alpha Persei Group, or Melotte 20. I find this cluster far more striking than even the Pleiades. It contains far more stars, of far more variation in brightness, color, and number. It also takes up the entire binocular field of view.

After you spend time on Melotte 20, it's time to hop over to the most subtle star cluster, M34, checking another Messier object off your list. While some books, such as Seronik's *Binocular Highlights*, list this as a winter target, it's far enough north that you might as well snag it during the fall. During winter, you'll probably be too distracted by M42.

OBSERVING LOG

Date: Time: Location:

Sky Conditions (Seeing/Transparency):

Instrument (Magnification/Aperture):

Notes:

Additional sketching circles are provided in the back of this book.

Object of Interest: M34
Dark Sky Requirement: Suburbs
Object Type: Open Cluster
Brightness: 5.2
Distance: 1,600 Light-Years
Apparent Size: 35 Arc Minutes

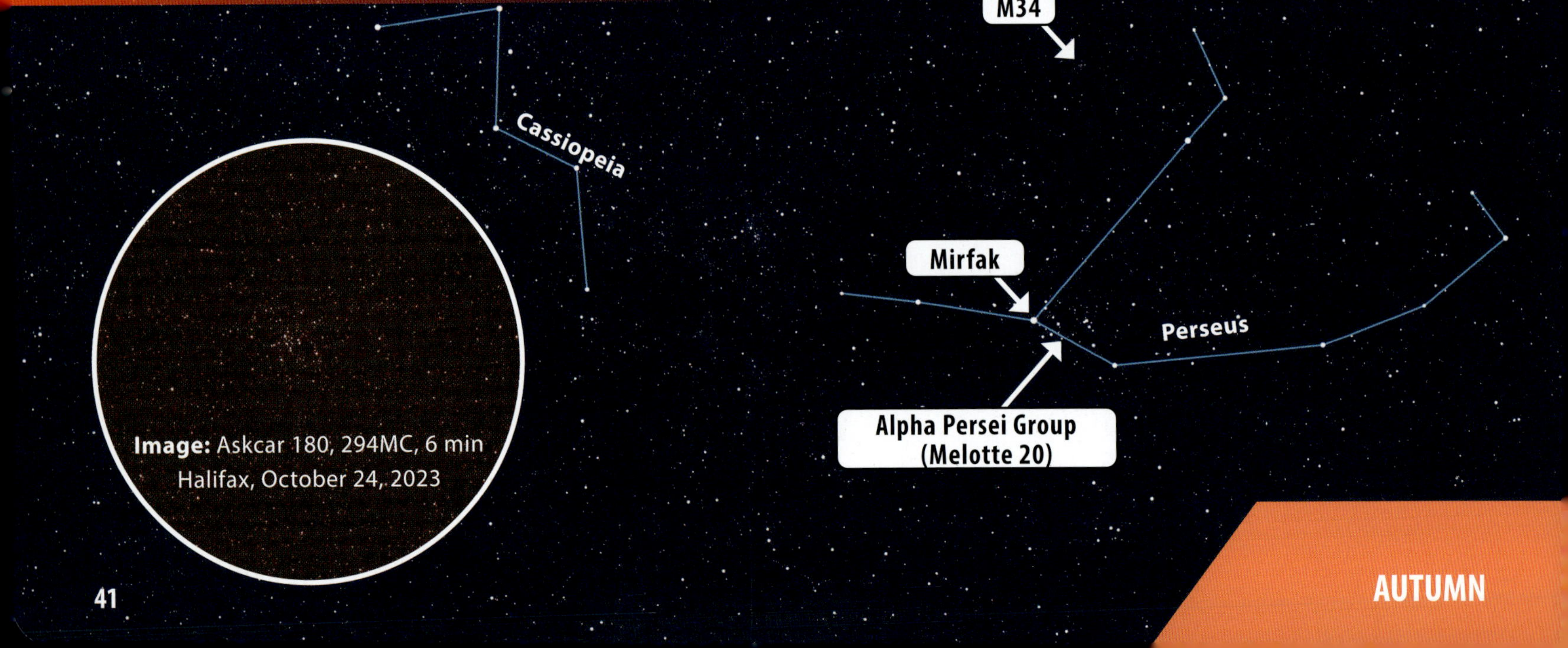

Image: Askcar 180, 294MC, 6 min Halifax, October 24, 2023

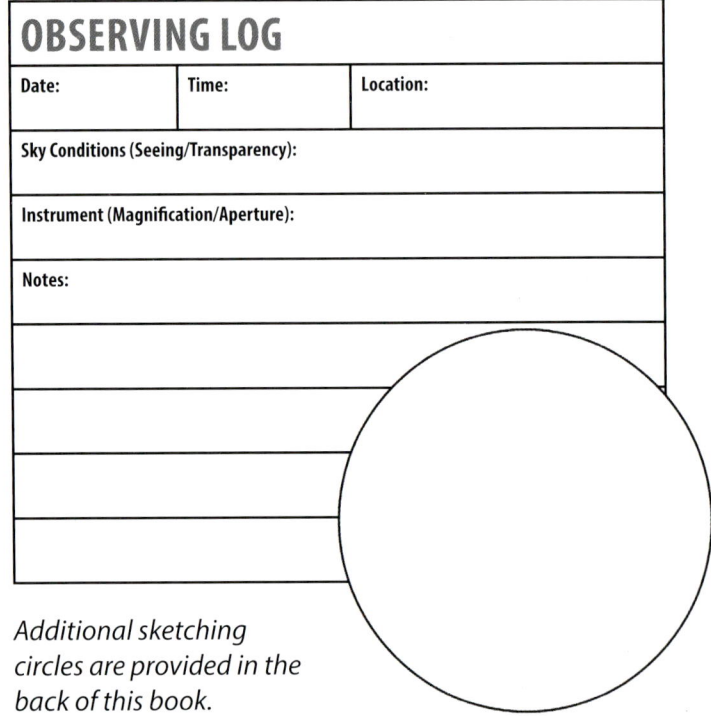

AUTUMN

Object of Interest: Alpha Persei Group (Melotte 20)
Dark Sky Requirement: Suburbs
Object Type: Open Cluster
Brightness: 2.3
Distance: 600 Light-Years
Apparent Size: 300 Arc Minutes

Image: Askcar 180, 294MC, 6 min, Halifax, October 24, 2023

WINTER TARGETS

The winter sky is filled with exciting targets for binoculars, even from the city. The focal point of the winter sky is definitely Orion. The distinct "three stars in a row," which most know as the Belt of Orion, is the most identifiable pattern of stars in the sky, possibly even more so than the Big Dipper.

The winter sky is dominated by an asterism known as the "Winter Hexagon" (or, if you include Betelgeuse, "the Big G"). The Milky Way passes right through this part of the sky, but it is notably sparse compared to the summer when we're looking towards the core.

Within Orion lies the Northern Hemisphere's most brilliant nebula, the Great Orion Nebula. It's well known by space fans that every December, images of the Orion Nebula from amateur astrophotographers testing out their new gear fill our social media feeds. The nebula is so bright that you don't even need binoculars to see it, but we'll talk about that more in the designated section.

Winter also includes two of our night sky's most spectacular stars. Sirius, the brightest star in the sky, is the cause of many UFO sightings. Betelgeuse, which is normally the brightest of the red giants in our sky. is a red giant star that varies in brightness over time. However, recently, it's been dimming significantly, and many astronomers are wondering if it's about ready to explode (in reality, this may not occur for another million years or so).

This color image of the Orion Nebula is a 1-hour exposure taken from the city. Although lacking in color through binoculars, your eyes will see considerable detail in this nebula, even from the suburbs.

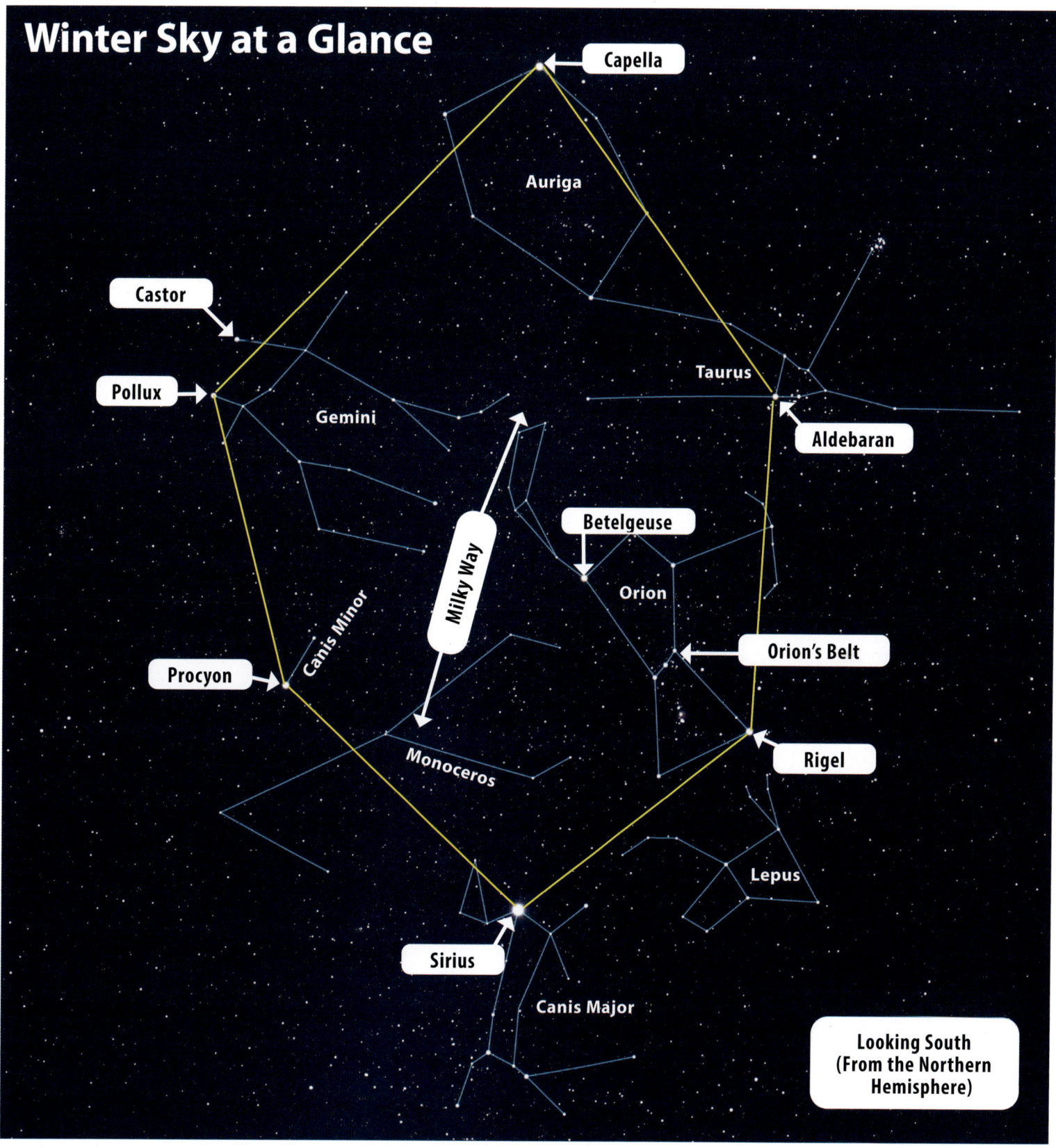

27. Winter Stars and Asterisms

As mentioned earlier, the Winter Hexagon is the largest asterism in the winter sky, and perhaps the largest asterism of all (Hawaiian star lines aside). This asterism is composed of Capella, Pollux, Procyon, Sirius, Rigel, and Aldebaran. Other stars of note include Castor (the head of the right twin in Gemini) and Betelgeuse. Some astronomers I know also have memorized the names of the stars in Orion's Belt—Alnitak, Alnilam, and Mintaka.

Some interesting binocular asterisms include Davis's Dog (which I first found in Stellarium), though this may have originated from a list created by astronomer David Ratledge and posted to his website listed in the footnote below.[1] Also from David's webpage was Lambda-Lambda, a pattern of stars that forms the Greek letter lambda, including the star named Lambda Orionis. "Carol's Smiley Face" borders open cluster M38 in Auriga. (Carol L is a frequent poster on Cloudy Nights, an online astronomy forum.)

---

[1] http://www.deep-sky.co.uk/asterisms.htm

Image: Askar 180, 2600MC, 3 min
Stargaze NS, May 25, 2024

Collindar 69
(Phi Orionis)
Lambda-Lambda

Image: Askar 180, 294MC, 9 min
Halifax, October 3 (AM), 2023

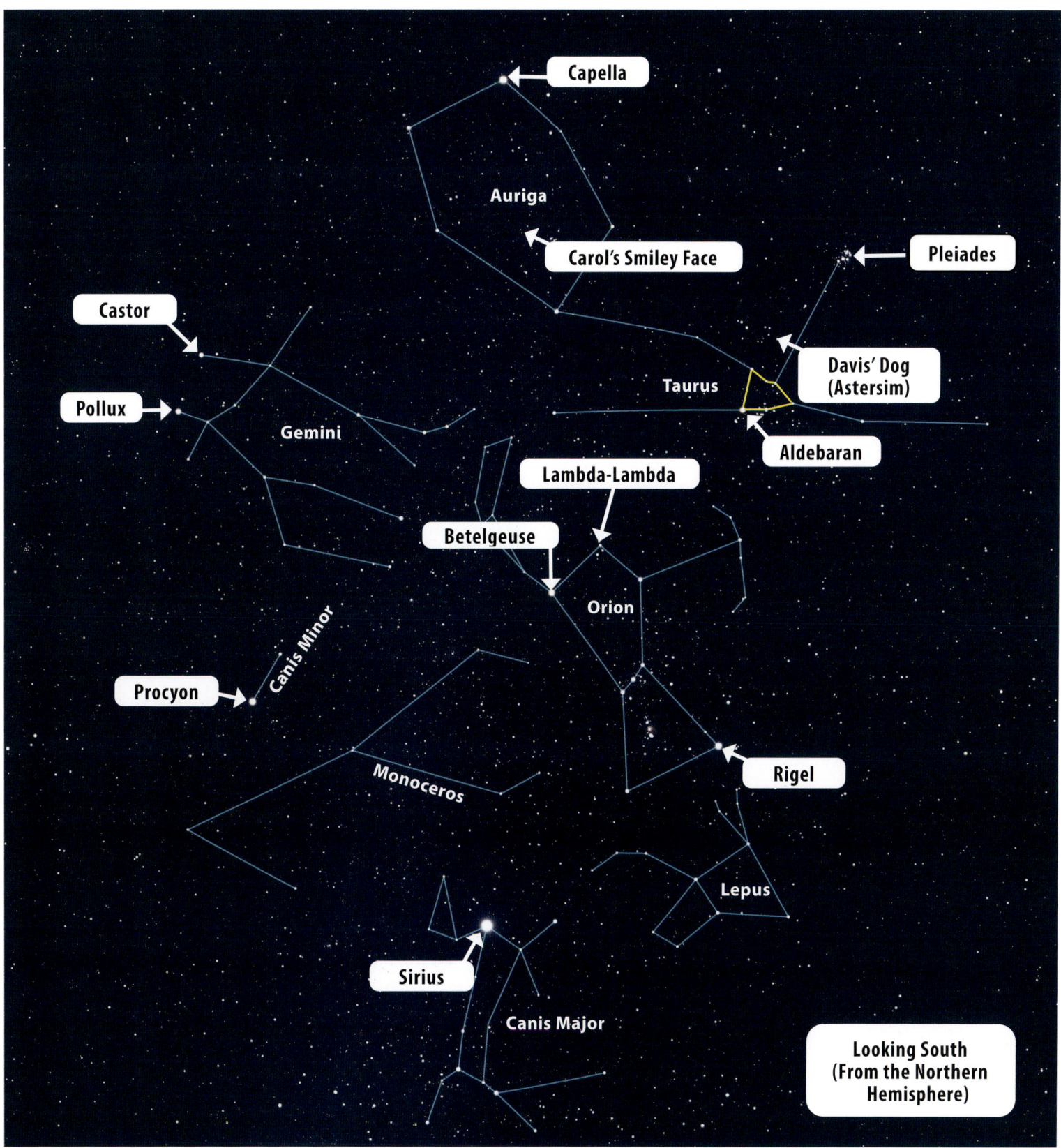

28. Hyades (Melotte 25)

At just over 150 light-years in distance, the Hyades is the closest star cluster. This is an open, or "galactic," cluster formed from stars born from the same cloud of gas at around the same time. These "young" (only a few hundred million years old) stars haven't been "perturbed" (yes, that's the official term) by gravity to the point that they spread amongst the other stars in our galaxy.

This cluster is accented by the bright star Aldebaran, which isn't actually part of the cluster at all. Aldebaran is a red giant star located about halfway between us and the Hyades. There is a lot to explore within this cluster. With binoculars, be sure to observe its many double stars and stars of various colors.

OBSERVING LOG

Date: Time: Location:

Sky Conditions (Seeing/Transparency):

Instrument (Magnification/Aperture):

Notes:

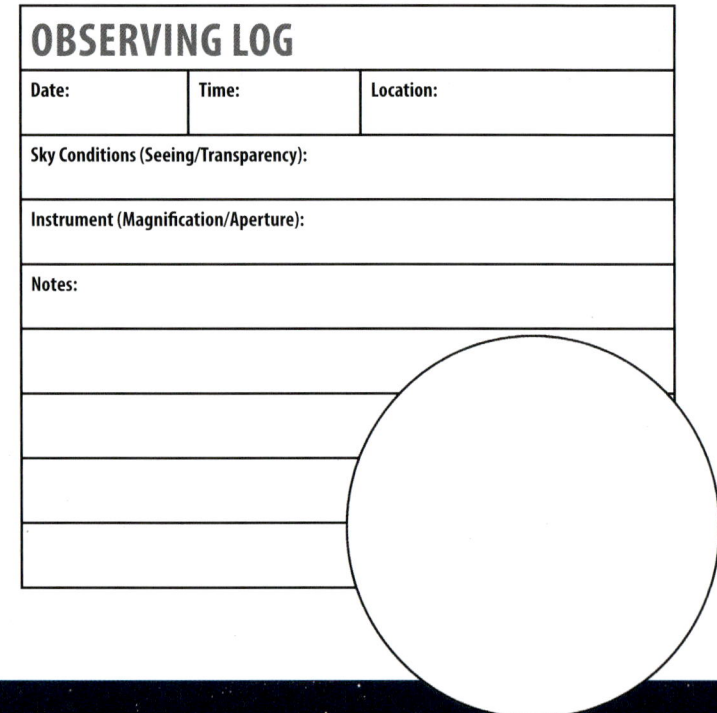

WINTER

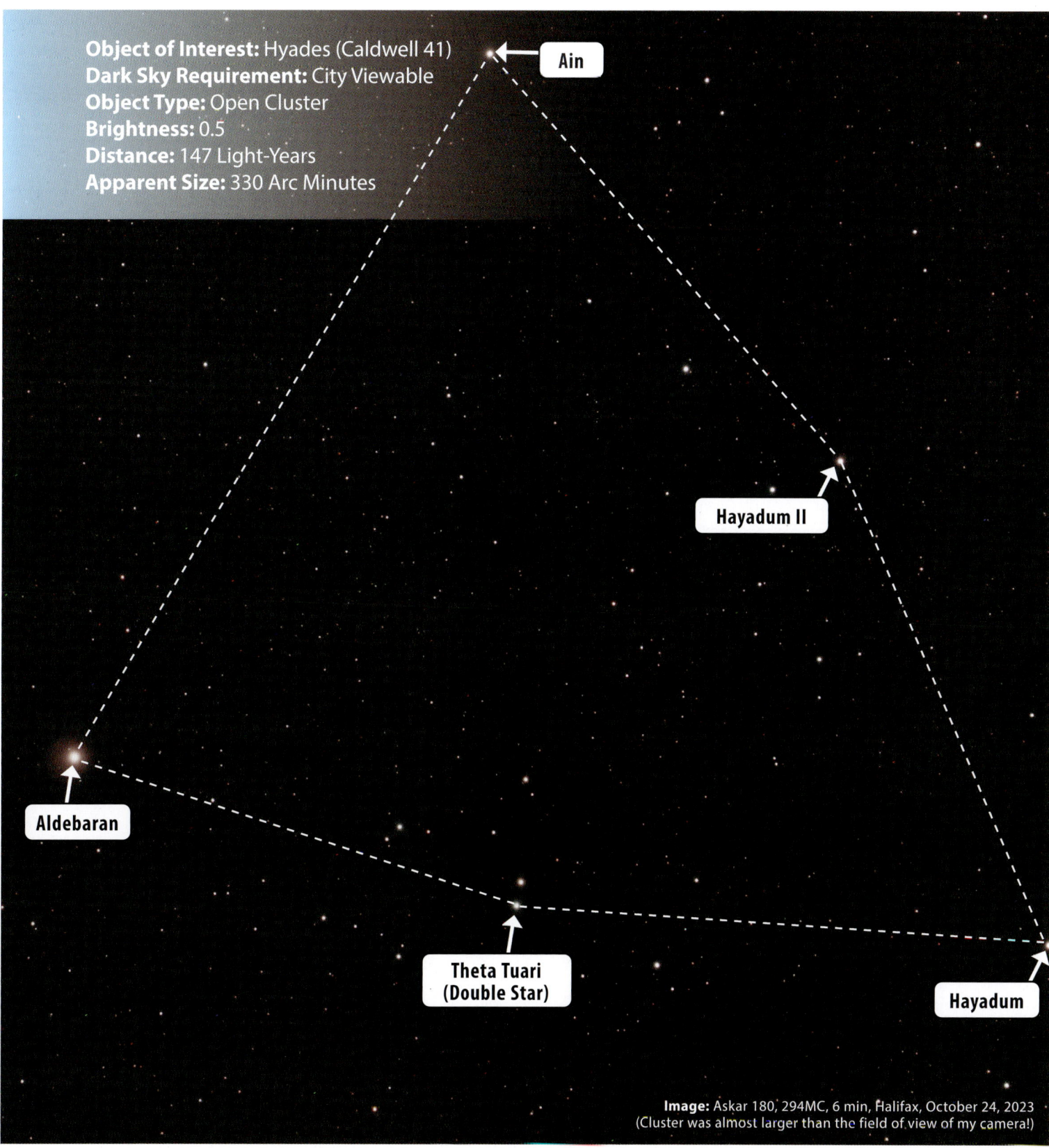

29. Pleiades (M45)

The Pleiades is the most recognizable object in the winter sky. However, many people mistakenly believe that this cluster is the "Little Dipper" asterism. Like the Hyades, this is an open star cluster; however, in the darkest skies (or with a camera from the city), clouds of gas can still be observed around these stars.

The Pleiades is much younger than the Hyades. Interestingly, the dust cloud surrounding it is not thought to have originated with the cluster and may have accumulated later during the cluster's journey through space (Gordon et al., 2003).

Though only six of the seven stars in the Pleiades are visible with the unaided eye, through binoculars, dozens more stars come into view, making this cluster appear even more beautiful.

OBSERVING LOG

Date:	Time:	Location:

Sky Conditions (Seeing/Transparency):

Instrument (Magnification/Aperture):

Notes:

Object of Interest: Pleiades (Seven Sisters, Subaru)
Dark Sky Requirement: City Viewable
Object Type: Open Cluster
Brightness: 1.5
Distance: 430 Light Years
Apparent Size: 120 Arc Minutes

Image: Askar 180, 294MC, 9 min Halifax, October 18, 2023

WINTER

30. M35

M35 is one of the more popular open clusters in the winter sky. In dark skies, it is visible without a telescope. However, I've sometimes had trouble picking it out in our urban skies, even with a small telescope.

Start by locating the stars Pollux and Castor, then trace out the entire constellation of Gemini (the Twins) with your eyes. Bringing up the binoculars on Castor's foot will reveal this cluster's brightest stars. If your skies are dark enough, neighboring star clusters will also occupy the same field of view.

Directly above Castor's foot is a sprawling cascade of stars called "Collinder 89" (or Cr 89 in stargazing software). The Collinder Catalog of star clusters includes such objects as the Coathanger (page 25) and even Orion's Belt.

OBSERVING LOG

Date: Time: Location:

Sky Conditions (Seeing/Transparency):

Instrument (Magnification/Aperture):

Notes:

Object of Interest: M35
Dark Sky Requirement: Suburbs
Object Type: Open Cluster
Brightness: 5.1
Distance: 3,000 Light-Years
Apparent Size: 40 Arc Minutes

Image: Askar 180, 294MC, 9 min Halifax, October 3, 2023

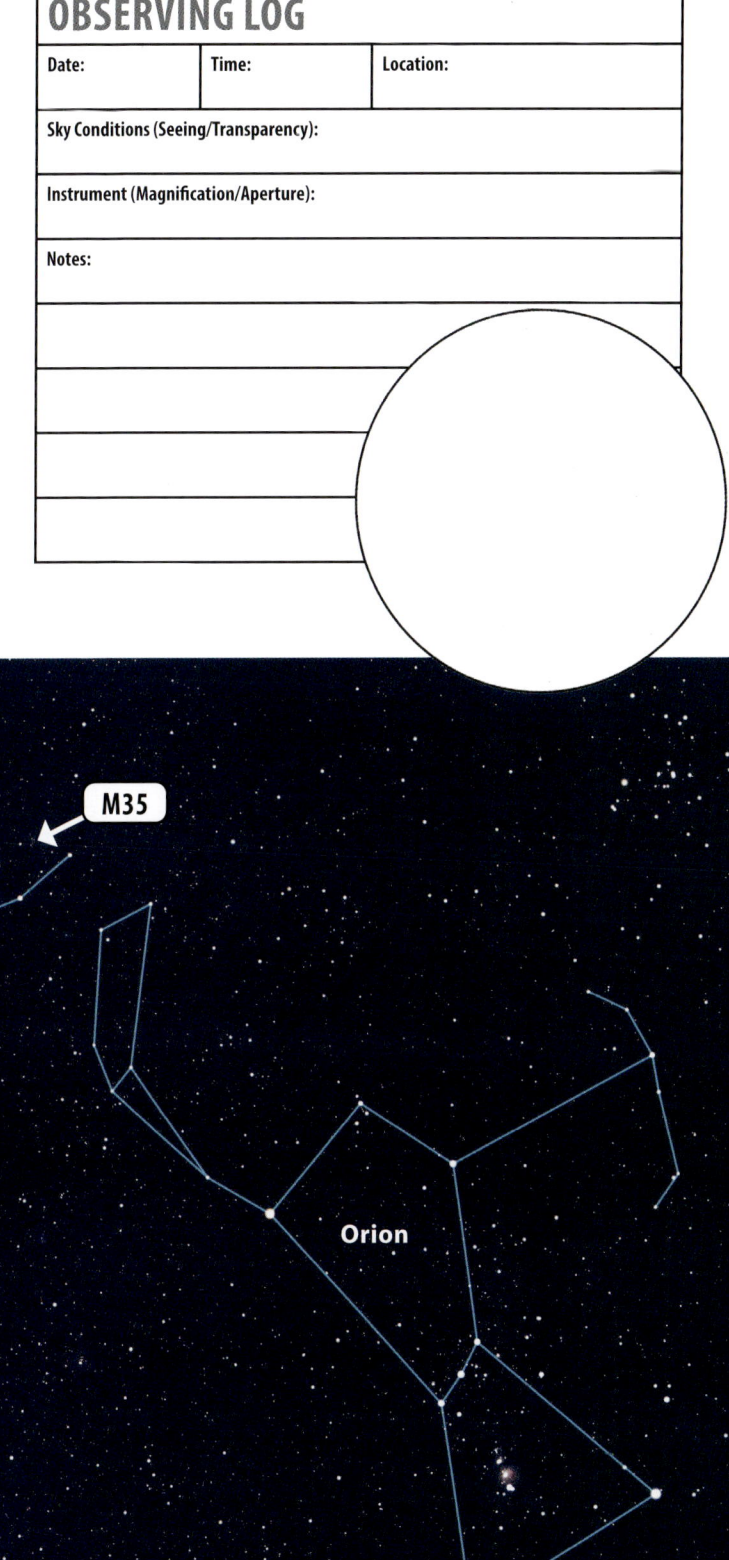

WINTER

31. The Orion Nebula (M42)

The crown jewel of stargazing targets, the Orion Nebula is by far the most popular stargazing target in the winter sky. Visible without a telescope as a smudge below Orion's Belt, the slightest bit of magnification brings the giant gas cloud to life in front of your eyes.

The Orion Nebula is known as a "Star Factory," a nursery where stars are born. It is made primarily of hydrogen gas, glowing in the light of young stars. Dust lanes crisscross the glowing background, a sign that these stars will form entire solar systems with planets and moons alike.

The binocular view is just the tip of the iceberg. The first time I saw the Orion Nebula in binoculars, I said, "Wow." The first time I saw the Orion Nebula in my 12-inch telescope, I ran into the house, yelling to everyone who would listen, "You've got to see this!"

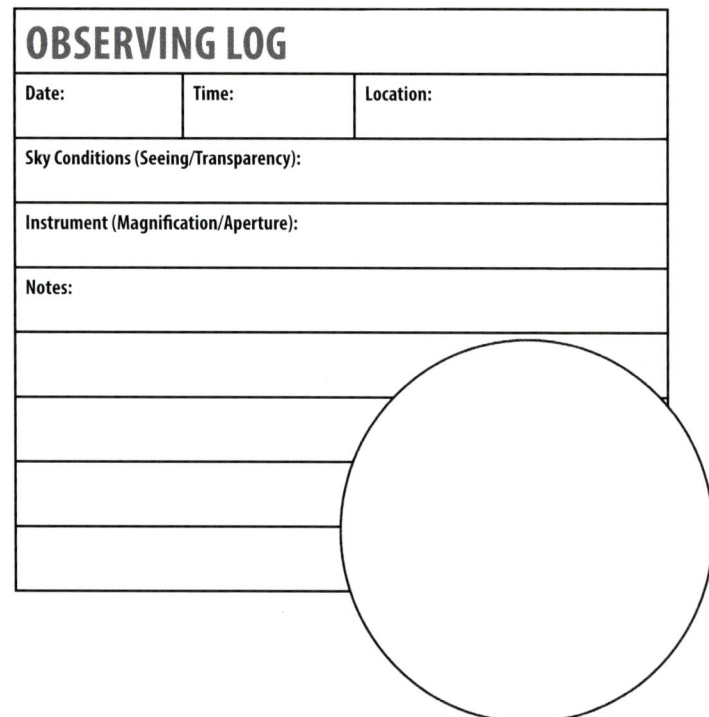

OBSERVING LOG

Date: Time: Location:

Sky Conditions (Seeing/Transparency):

Instrument (Magnification/Aperture):

Notes:

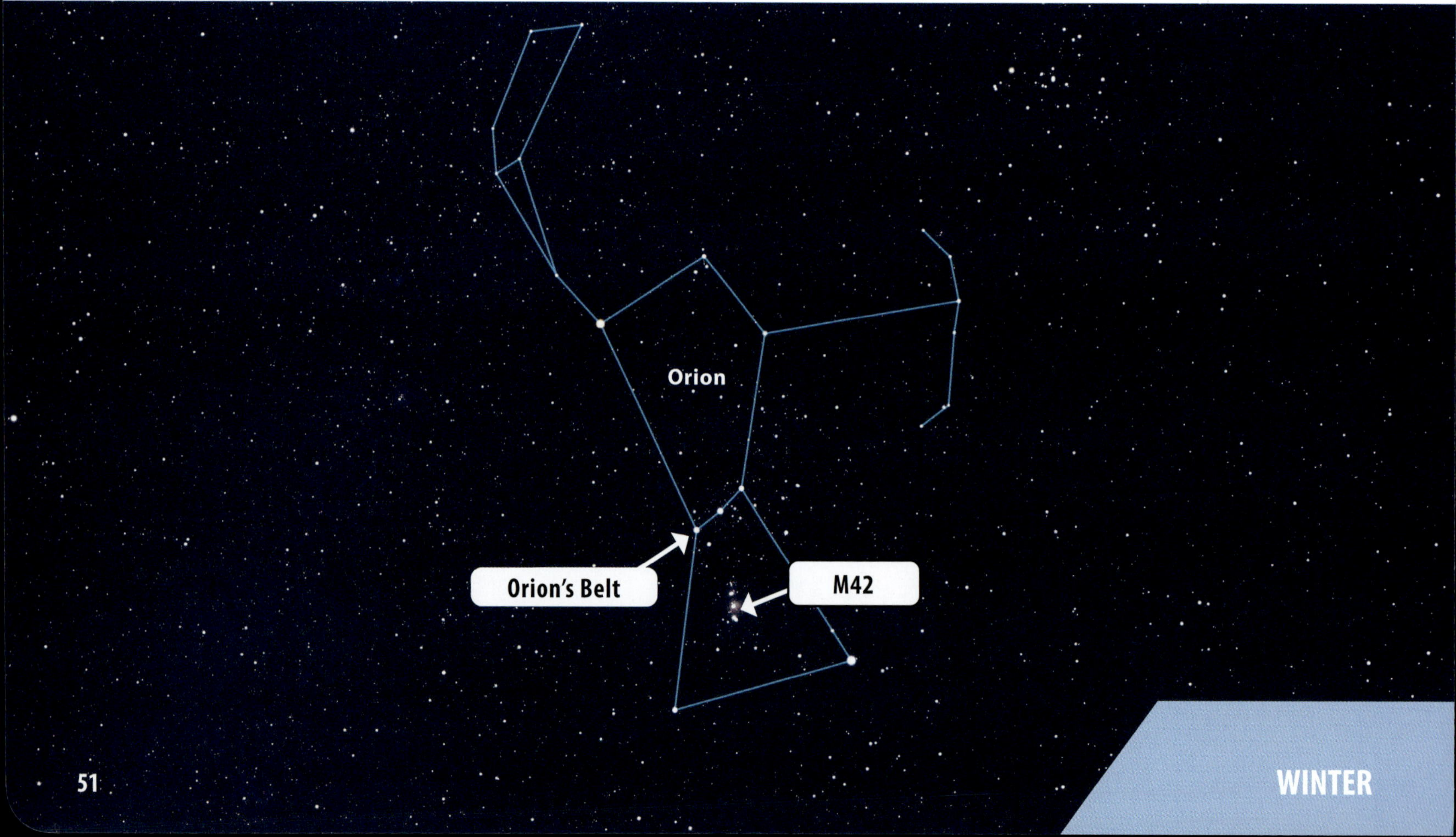

WINTER

Object of Interest: The Orion Nebula (M42)
Dark Sky Requirement: City Viewable
Object Type: Star-Forming Nebula
Brightness: 4.0
Distance: 1,400 Light-Years
Apparent Size: 85 x 60 Arc Minutes

Image: Askar 180, 294MC, 15 min, Halifax, October 3, 2023
(Saturation reduced to match view through binoculars)

32. Little Beehive (M41) and M47

M41, the Little Beehive, gets its name from its similarity to M44, the Beehive Cluster in Cancer. M41 and M44 do look quite similar, although M41 is missing the obvious little "house" shape that defines M44. If you can see M41, M44 is most likely also in the sky. Despite M44 being categorized as a "springtime" target, it is quite close to Gemini, a winter constellation. Be sure to compare and contrast these two clusters.

M47 is a tight grouping of stars wedged between two reddish stars. If your skies are dark enough, you should see M46, a larger yet dimmer cluster, within the same field of view. This part of the sky is within the plane of the Milky Way Galaxy. Despite the fact that we're looking opposite the core of our galaxy, there are still dozens of star clusters in the area, so be sure to keep exploring after you've checked the brightest targets off your list.

OBSERVING LOG

Date: | Time: | Location:

Sky Conditions (Seeing/Transparency):

Instrument (Magnification/Aperture):

Notes:

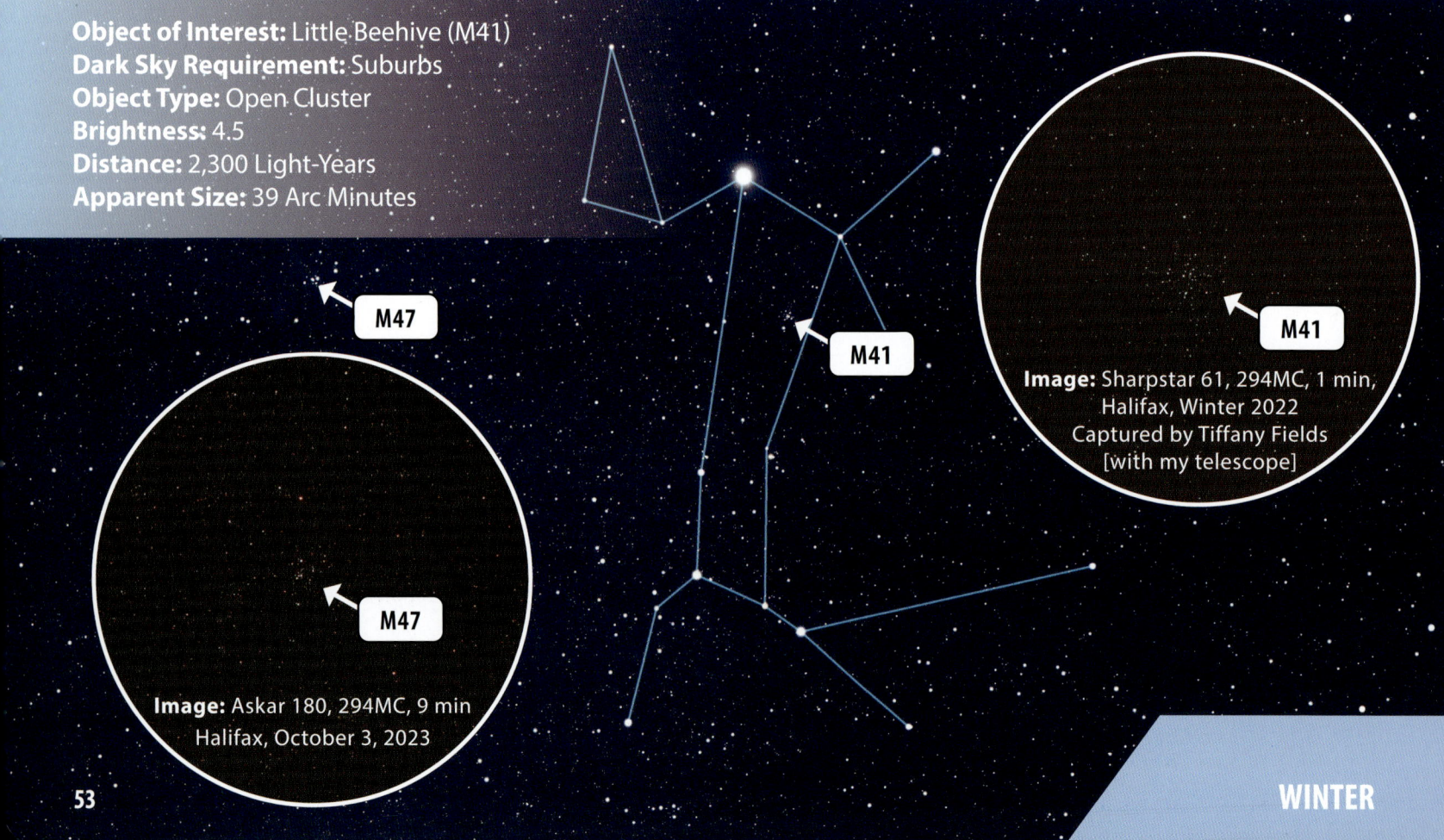

Object of Interest: Little Beehive (M41)
Dark Sky Requirement: Suburbs
Object Type: Open Cluster
Brightness: 4.5
Distance: 2,300 Light-Years
Apparent Size: 39 Arc Minutes

M47

Image: Sharpstar 61, 294MC, 1 min, Halifax, Winter 2022
Captured by Tiffany Fields
[with my telescope]

M41

M47

Image: Askar 180, 294MC, 9 min Halifax, October 3, 2023

WINTER

33. Auriga Clusters (M36, M37, M38)

The Auriga star clusters are quite easy to find. Simply point the binoculars in the middle of Auriga and pan around. If your skies are dark, you can't miss them. M36 can fit into the same field of view as either M38 or M37 at 10x. Panning back and forth between M37 and M38 allows you to contrast these three clusters nicely.

I've often asked students at the observatory to come up with new names for these clusters. The "Turtle" seems to be a popular choice for M36. I like to call M37 the "Cloaking Warbird." Stellarium calls M38 the "Starfish," which I think is pretty fitting.

You may have already visited this section of sky to observe Carol's Smiley Face. Nearby, you may also see Collinder 63, a cluster Stellarium refers to as "The Letter Y." Can you guess why?

Object of Interest: Starfish Cluster (M38)
Dark Sky Requirement: Suburbs
Object Type: Open Cluster
Brightness: 6.4
Distance: 4,600 Light-Years
Apparent Size: 20 Arc Minutes

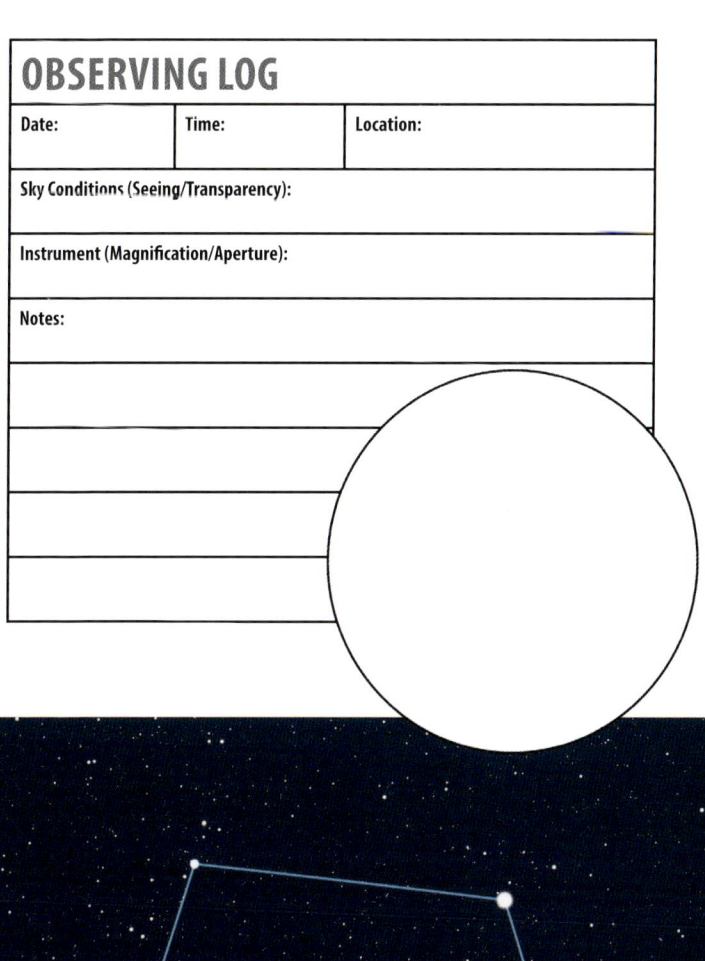

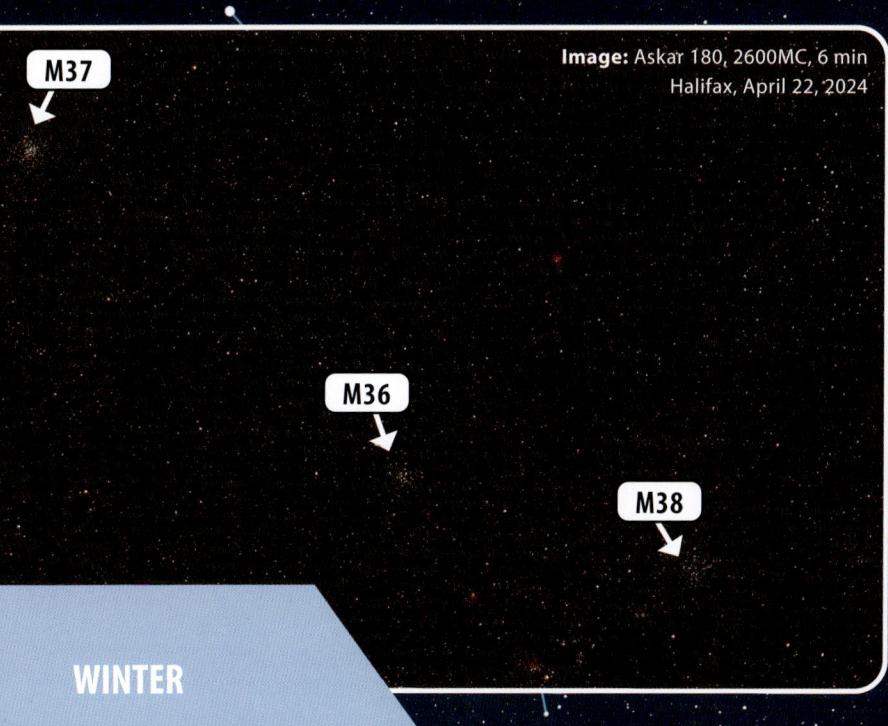

Image: Askar 180, 2600MC, 6 min
Halifax, April 22, 2024

OBSERVING LOG

Date: Time: Location:
Sky Conditions (Seeing/Transparency):
Instrument (Magnification/Aperture):
Notes:

WINTER

34. Winter Double Stars

Most of the double stars on this list (and most binocular double star lists) include stars that appear close together in the sky but are not actually gravitationally bound to each other. We call these stars optical doubles because this is simply a chance alignment based on Earth's location in the galaxy. That said, many double stars are found within star clusters. For example, Phi Orionis is part of an open star cluster called Collinder 69.

The sky is teeming with double stars, and the challenge lies in finding those that are truly beautiful, ones worth revisiting. The astronomer William Herschel cataloged over five thousand double stars that he found worthy of exploration. This is why I've chosen stars like 15 CMa, a bright blue star with a few neighbors to contrast its color, and Sigma Orionis, which, along with five neighboring stars, resembles a sword, or a parade of colorful stars streaking through Auriga.

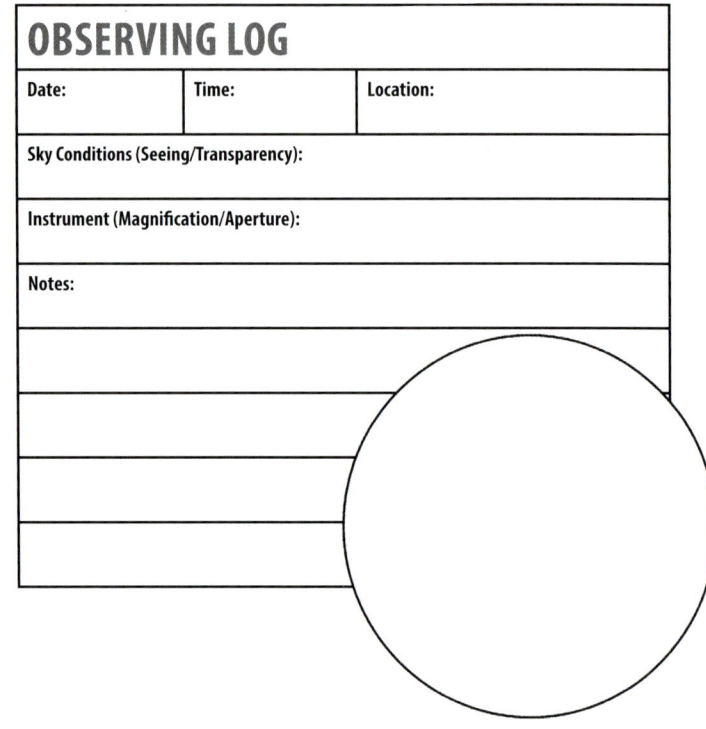

OBSERVING LOG

Date: Time: Location:

Sky Conditions (Seeing/Transparency):

Instrument (Magnification/Aperture):

Notes:

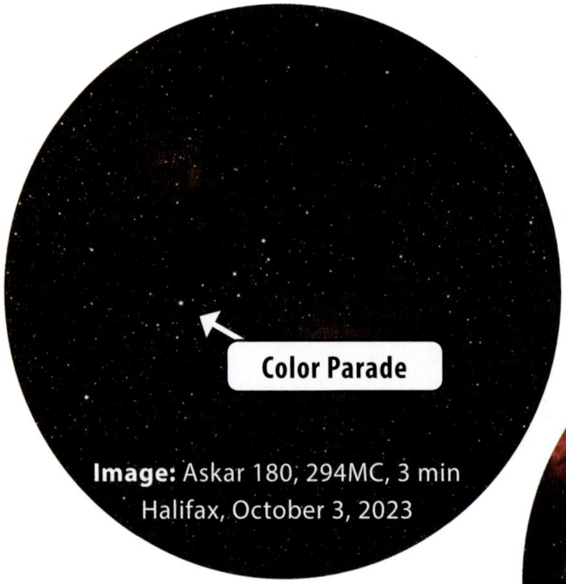

Color Parade
Image: Askar 180, 294MC, 3 min
Halifax, October 3, 2023

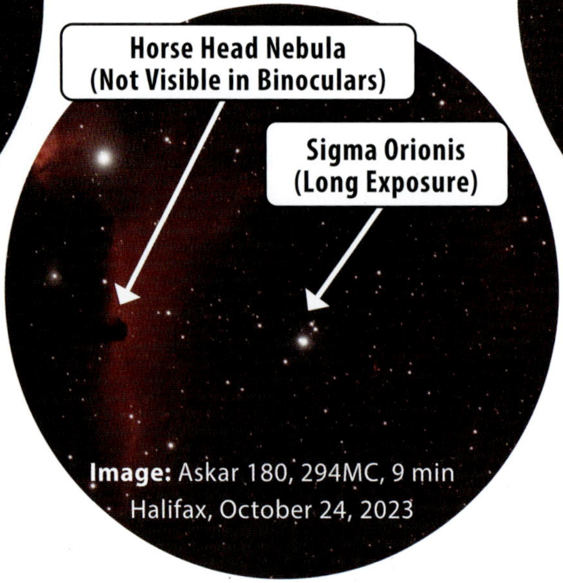

Horse Head Nebula (Not Visible in Binoculars)
Sigma Orionis (Long Exposure)
Image: Askar 180, 294MC, 9 min
Halifax, October 24, 2023

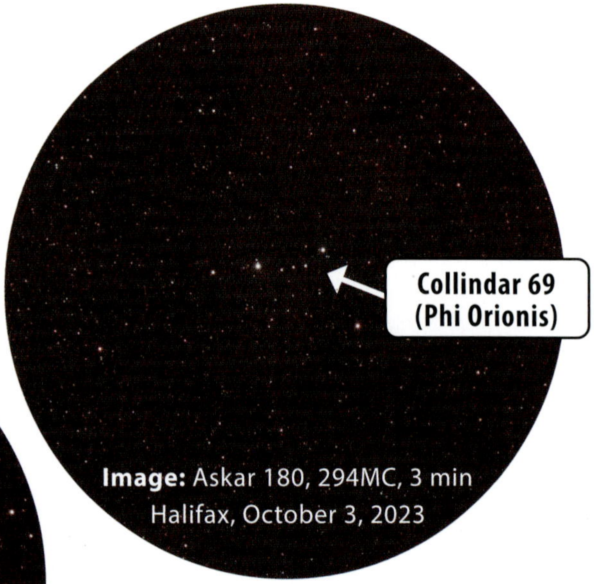

Collindar 69 (Phi Orionis)
Image: Askar 180, 294MC, 3 min
Halifax, October 3, 2023

WINTER

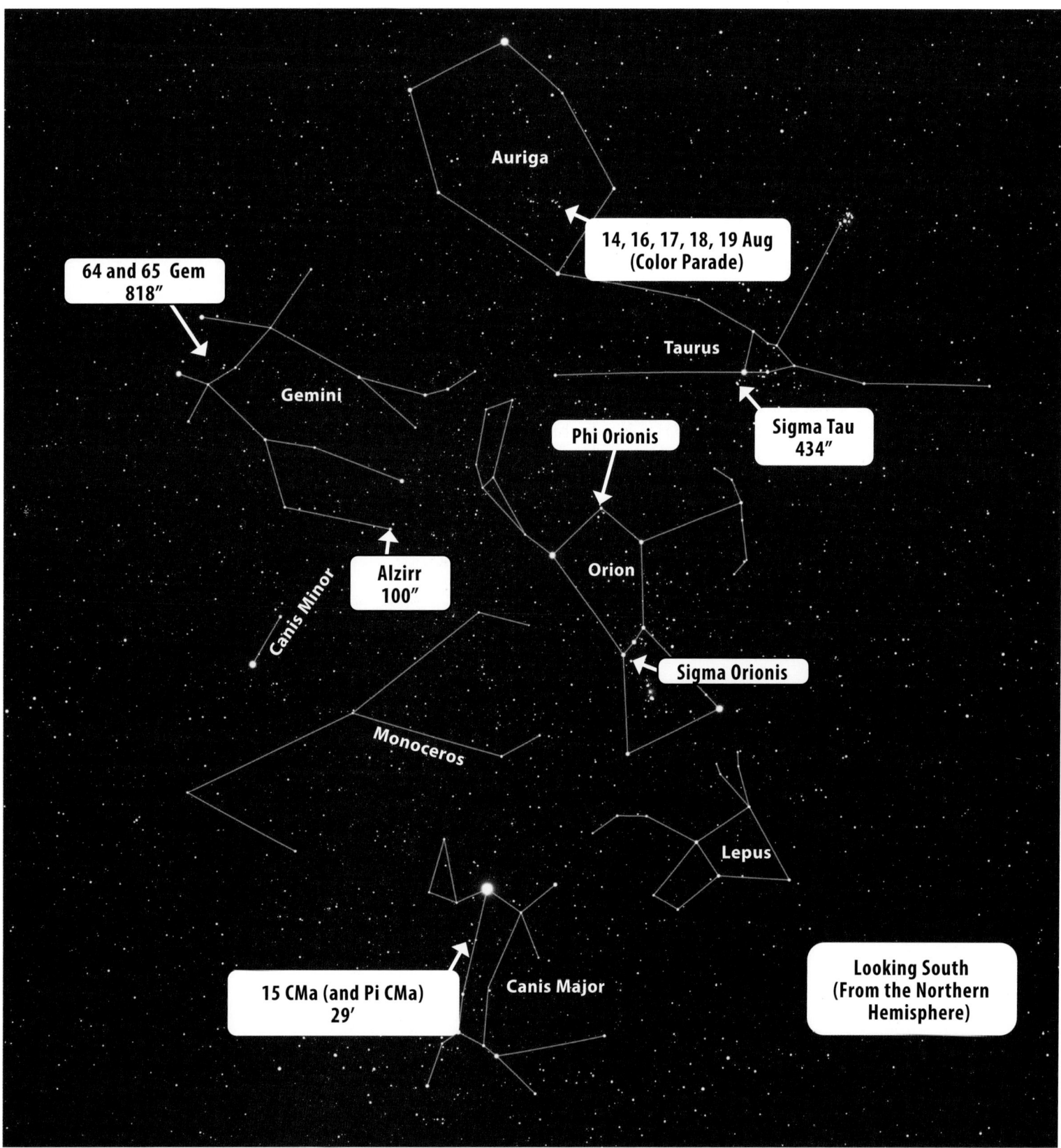

SPRING TARGETS

I think of springtime as the "short" season for astronomy. From my backyard in the city, there is only a narrow window between my neighbor's house and a giant tree where I do my stargazing from home. A streetlight also stands between this house and the tree, so I often resort to using our shed to block the light, further limiting my view of the sky.

I mention this because during springtime, the days are getting longer and the nights are getting shorter. Amateur astronomers really notice how these lengthening days cut into our stargazing opportunities, especially when the days are getting warmer and we actually want to be outside for once. Due to these factors, sometimes I feel like I miss out on the springtime sky altogether.

The other challenge with spring stargazing is that the core of the Milky Way doesn't rise until late at night with the summer constellations. When observing in the spring, you either need very dark skies, or to be okay with a limited number of targets. When I was taking the images for this section, I was under mostly dark skies. They were technically Bortle 4, but with dry air and no moon, I was able to see several galaxies, including the Leo Trio, without much difficulty.

Springtime is the perfect time to practice "Arc to Arcturus, Spike to Spica" as this helps you to identify two of the three stars in the Spring Triangle.

This Digital Sky Survey (DSS) image of the Virgo Cluster shows just how many galaxies are located in this part of the sky. However, unless you have perfectly dark skies, most of these targets are outside the range of binoculars.

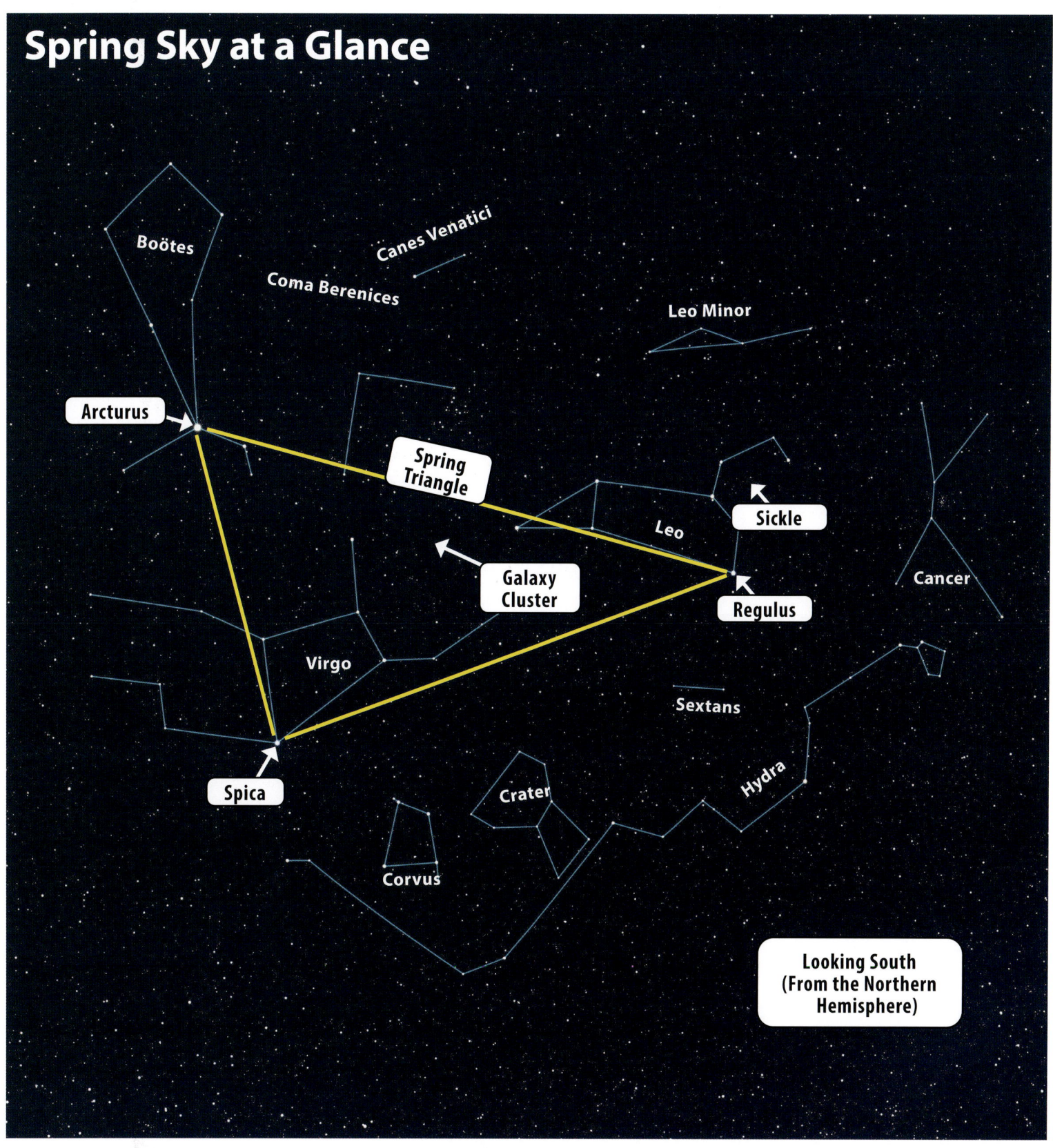

35. Spring Stars and Asterisms

There are only a handful of springtime stars that a seasoned amateur astronomer typically knows by heart. Bright orange Arcturus is the most well-known, often remembered as "Arc to Arcturus." Arcturus, Regulus, and Spica form what is known as the Spring Triangle. If you can recognize the three diamond asterisms (in Virgo, Corvus, and Crater) and the sickle (in Leo), you've pretty much got the springtime sky covered.

In terms of binocular asterisms, there are a few fun targets from the Milwaukee Astronomical Society's website. These include the Fly Swatter and the Sea Horse, with the Sea Horse located near the tip of Hydra's tail (use Corvus as a guide), and the Fly Swatter near the middle of the snake. Look for a very red star, U Hydrae (a carbon star), located under the Fly Swatter.

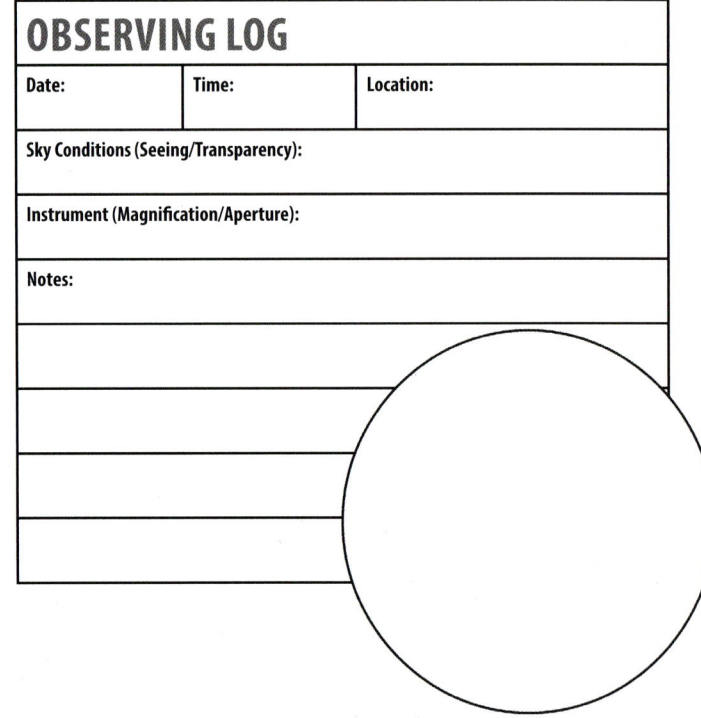

OBSERVING LOG

Date: Time: Location:

Sky Conditions (Seeing/Transparency):

Instrument (Magnification/Aperture):

Notes:

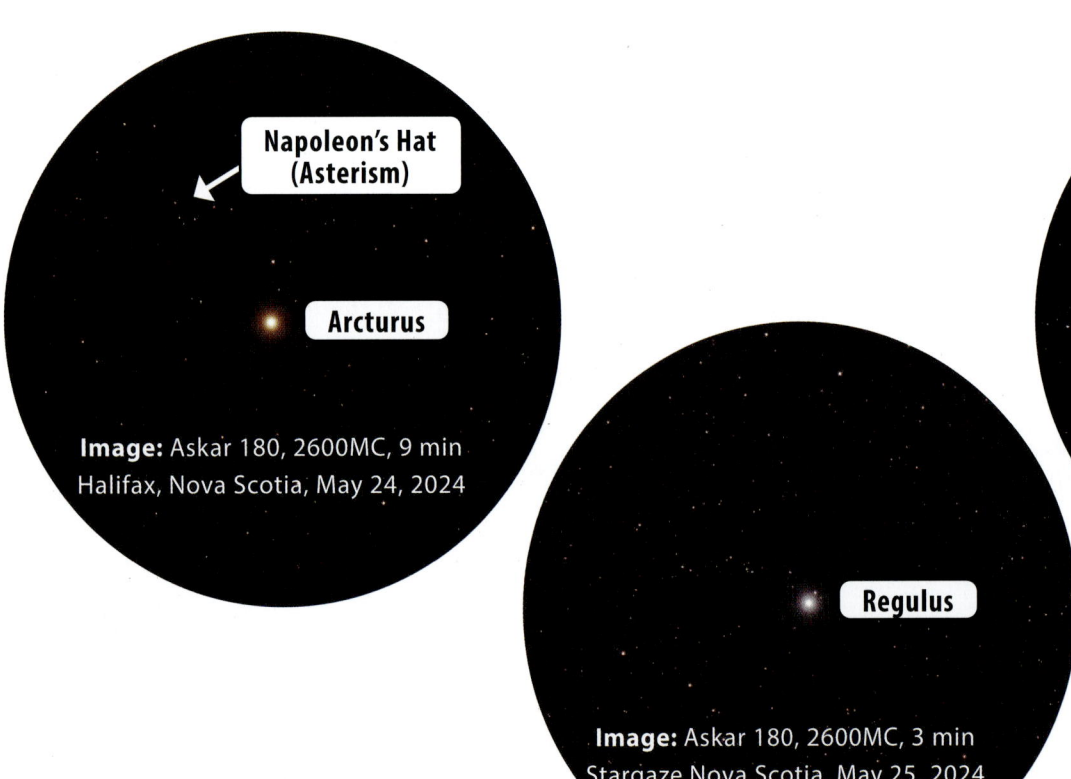

Image: Askar 180, 2600MC, 9 min
Halifax, Nova Scotia, May 24, 2024

Image: Askar 180, 2600MC, 3 min
Stargaze Nova Scotia, May 25, 2024

Image: Askar 180, 2600MC, 3 min
Stargaze Nova Scotia, May 25, 2024

SPRING

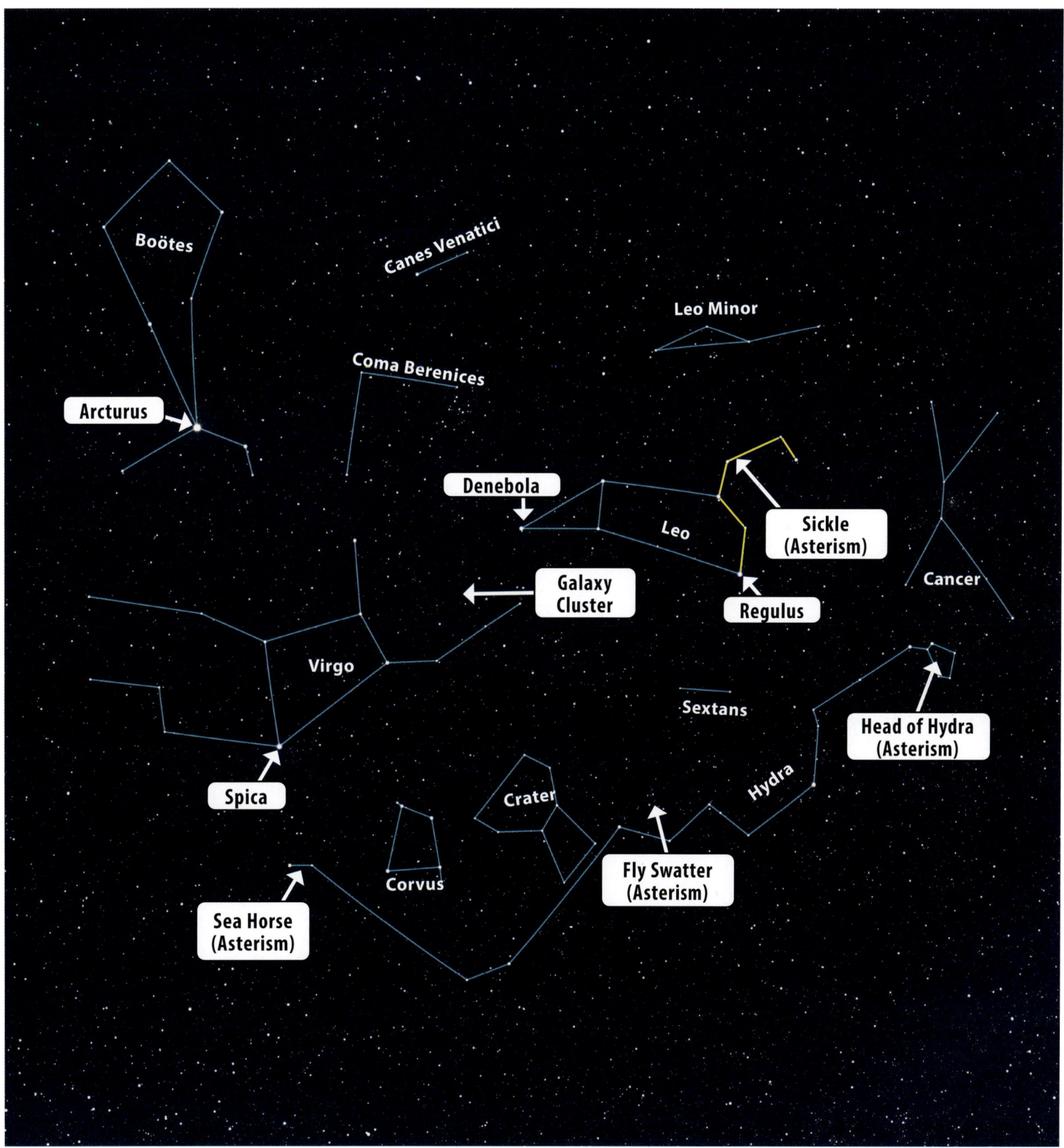

36. Globular Cluster (M3)

Springtime globular clusters M3 and M5 are surprisingly bright. I usually locate M3 by forming an equilateral triangle between Arcturus and Rho Boötes. It's worth noting that binoculars are too small to resolve individual stars within globular clusters. In fact, it wasn't until about two hundred years ago that telescopes became powerful enough to resolve stars in these clusters at all. (William Herschel was the first to accomplish this.)

Through binoculars, you'll notice that the cluster is closely surrounded by three "bright" stars. I use the term "bright" here relative to the cluster's brightness, but these stars are actually of 9th and 10th magnitude.

OBSERVING LOG

Date: Time: Location:

Sky Conditions (Seeing/Transparency):

Instrument (Magnification/Aperture):

Notes:

Object of Interest: M3
Dark Sky Requirement: Suburbs
Object Type: Globular Cluster
Brightness: 6.2
Distance: 33,000 Light-Years
Apparent Size: 18 Arc Minutes

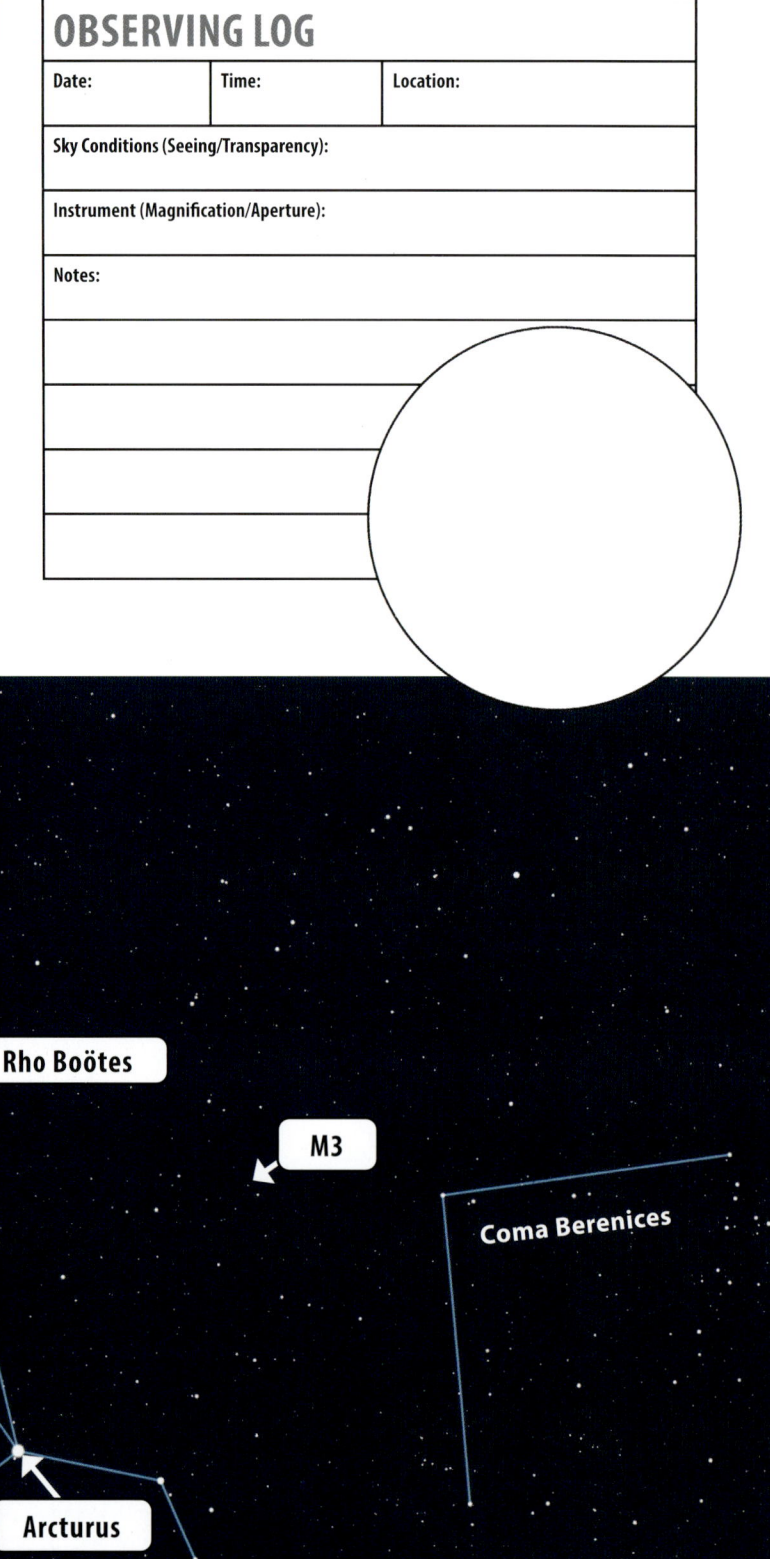

Image: Askcar 180, 2600MC, 18 min Halifax, April 19, 2024

SPRING

37. The Rose Cluster (M5)

Globular cluster M5 is actually slightly brighter than summer's M13 (5.7 vs. 5.8) and can be seen with the unaided eye from dark locations. However, that doesn't necessarily make it easier to see in binoculars from the suburbs. Surface brightness and the distance from the horizon also play a factor in observability. The surface brightness of a deep-sky object is essentially its brightness divided by its area. In other words, an object can be "bright" but appear dim if spread out over a large area.

The nice thing about M5 is that it is positioned close to the relatively bright star 5 Serpens, which can be seen without a telescope in dark skies. Many people call this cluster "The Rose," but I was unable to find the source. Astronomer Stephen O'Meara observes "Curved Wings" of stars, a pattern recognized earlier by the Earl of Rosse, an Irish astronomer from whom this nickname may have originated.

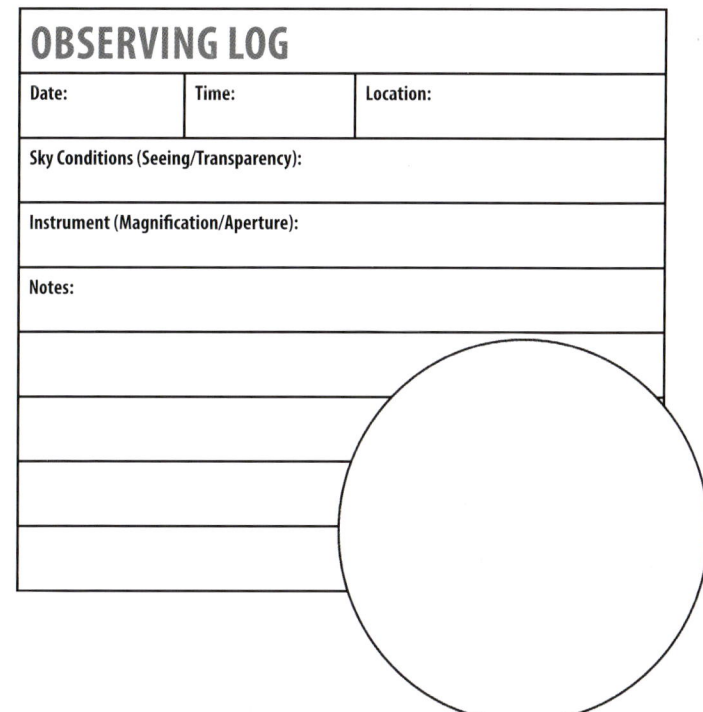

OBSERVING LOG

Date: Time: Location:

Sky Conditions (Seeing/Transparency):

Instrument (Magnification/Aperture):

Notes:

Object of Interest: M5
Dark Sky Requirement: Suburbs
Object Type: Globular Cluster
Brightness: 5.7
Distance: 24,000 Light-Years
Apparent Size: 23 Arc Minutes

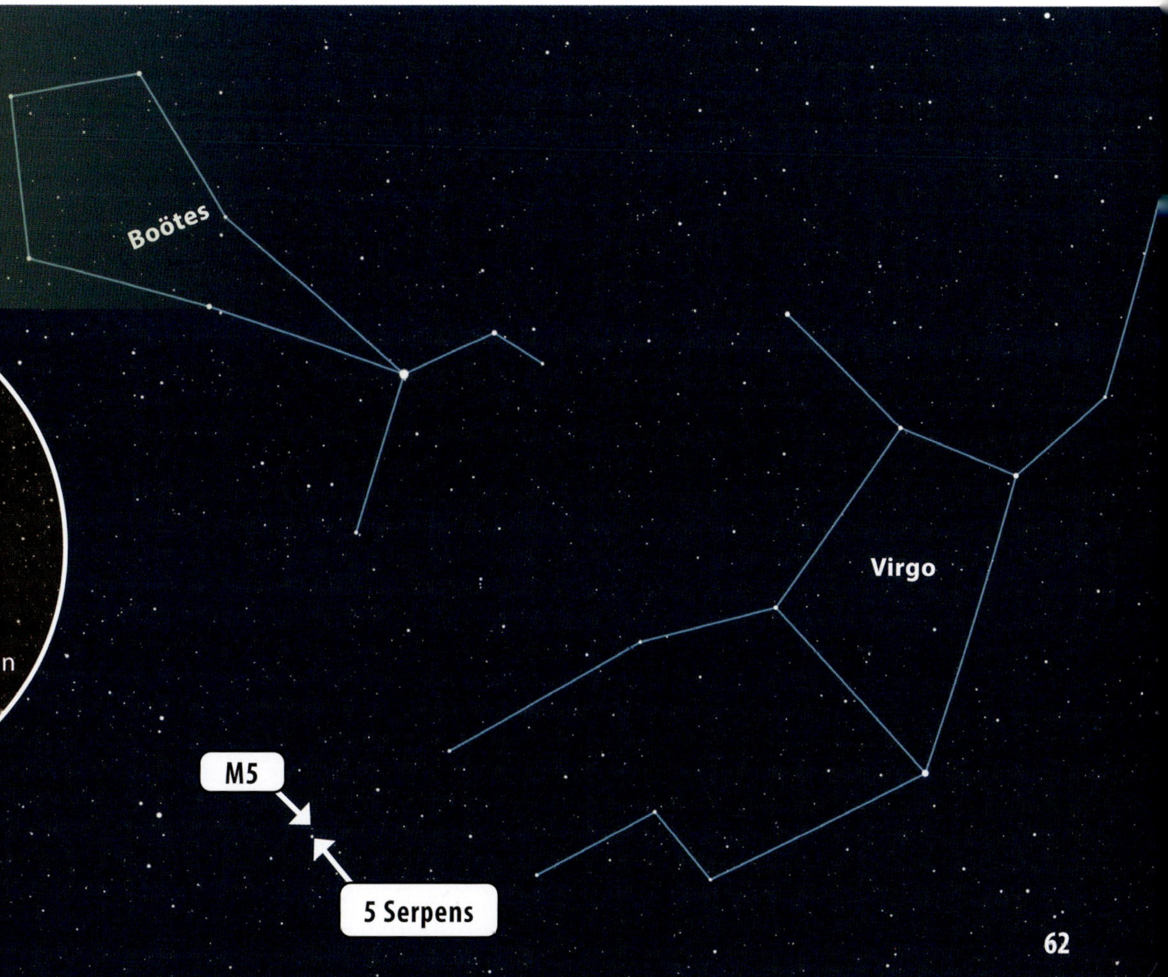

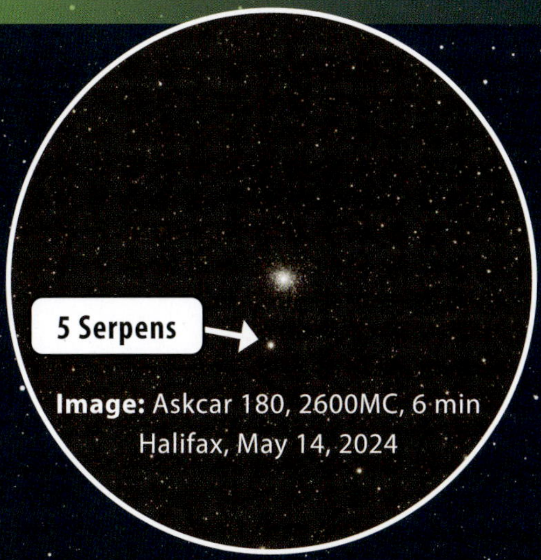

5 Serpens

Image: Askcar 180, 2600MC, 6 min Halifax, May 14, 2024

Boötes

Virgo

M5

5 Serpens

SPRING

38. The Beehive (M44)

The stars in Cancer are fairly dim. The cluster itself is actually brighter than the stars that form the surrounding constellation! That said, with binoculars, the Beehive Cluster is clearly identifiable in most conditions and can even be seen with the unaided eye from a dark location. Or, if you're an extreme stargazer like Stephen O'Meara, "while observing at 14,000 ft, I gazed at the Beehive without optical aid while occasionally breathing oxygen through an oxygen mask. The individual cluster members stood out boldly as rock-steady pearls."

When I'm looking for M44 from the city, I usually point my binoculars at Leo and simply pan toward the west. I identify this cluster by the distinct "house" pattern in the brightest five stars. I originally assumed this was meant to represent a bee smoker residing near the hive.

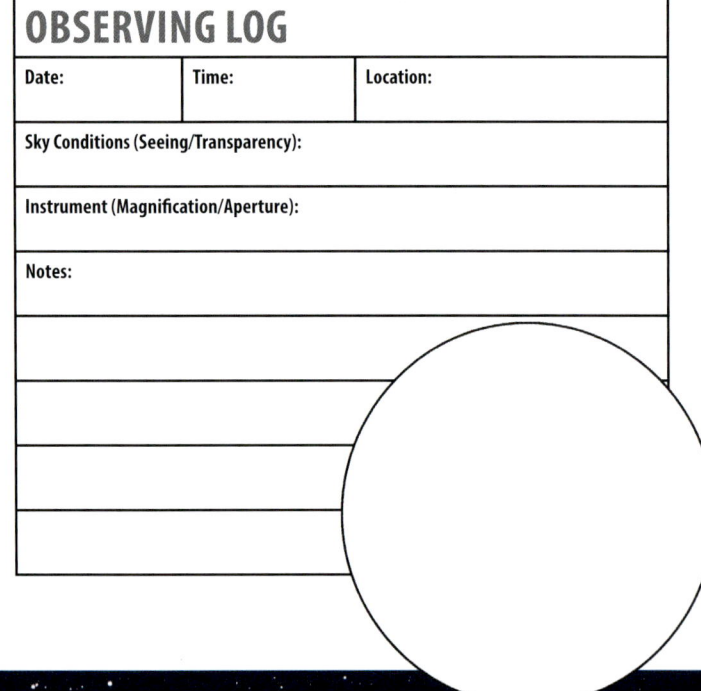

OBSERVING LOG

Date:　　　　Time:　　　　Location:

Sky Conditions (Seeing/Transparency):

Instrument (Magnification/Aperture):

Notes:

Object of Interest: The Beehive (M44)
Dark Sky Requirement: City Viewable
Object Type: Open Cluster
Brightness: 3.1
Distance: 313 Light-Years
Apparent Size: 120 Arc Minutes

Image: Askcar 180, 2600MC, 12 min Stargaze NS, May 25, 2024

SPRING

39. The Sombrero and the Arrow

From a dark location, the Sombrero galaxy will appear as a tiny grey gash in the sky. Telescope users often find M104 by using a bright star pattern nicknamed the "Pistol" nearby. The Pistol is quite small, so binocular observers will probably find another star pattern more helpful.

From Gary Seronik's *Binocular Highlights*, "The Arrow" is the preferred alternative star pattern. This pattern includes a triangle of bright stars that point toward a tight grouping of three stars, which altogether points toward the Pistol and M104.

Although the Sombrero is magnitude 8, most of its light is concentrated in a narrow slit. I've been able to capture a glimpse of this galaxy from surprisingly bright skies, including Saint John, New Brunswick.

OBSERVING LOG

Date: Time: Location:

Sky Conditions (Seeing/Transparency):

Instrument (Magnification/Aperture):

Notes:

Object of Interest: M104
Dark Sky Requirement: Suburbs
Object Type: Edge-on Spiral Galaxy
Brightness: 8.1
Distance: 28 Million Light-Years
Apparent Size: 8.4 x 4.9 Arc Minutes

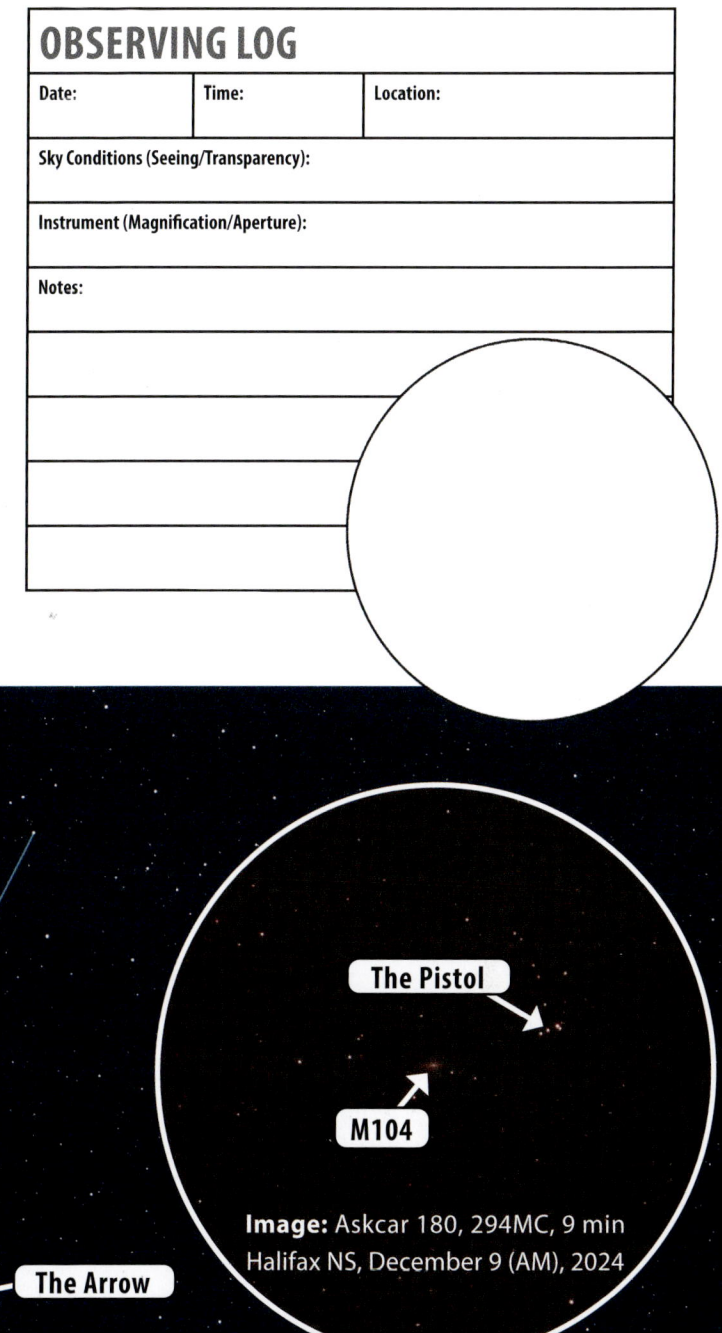

Image: Askcar 180, 294MC, 9 min
Halifax NS, December 9 (AM), 2024

SPRING

40. Coma Star Cluster (Melotte 111)

The Coma Star Cluster, also known as Melotte 111 or Collinder 256, extends beyond the field of view of most telescopes, making it an ideal cluster for binoculars. Keep an eye out for the distinctive "A" or tent-shaped pattern formed by the bright stars within the cluster. Let this cluster serve as a timely reminder that camping season is just around the corner.

The Coma Star Cluster is located on the edge of a literal zoo of galaxies known as the Virgo Cluster. Remember that seeing galaxies depends largely on the darkness of your skies and other factors such as the seeing conditions and the size of your optics. The closest notable galaxy to Melotte 111 is known as the "Needle Galaxy" or Caldwell 38. If you recall, the Caldwell list is an alternative to the Messier list, created by British astronomer Sir Patrick Moore.

OBSERVING LOG

Date: Time: Location:

Sky Conditions (Seeing/Transparency):

Instrument (Magnification/Aperture):

Notes:

Object of Interest: Coma Star Cluster
Dark Sky Requirement: City Viewable
Object Type: Open Cluster
Brightness: 1.8
Distance: 313 Light-Years
Apparent Size: 120 Arc Minutes

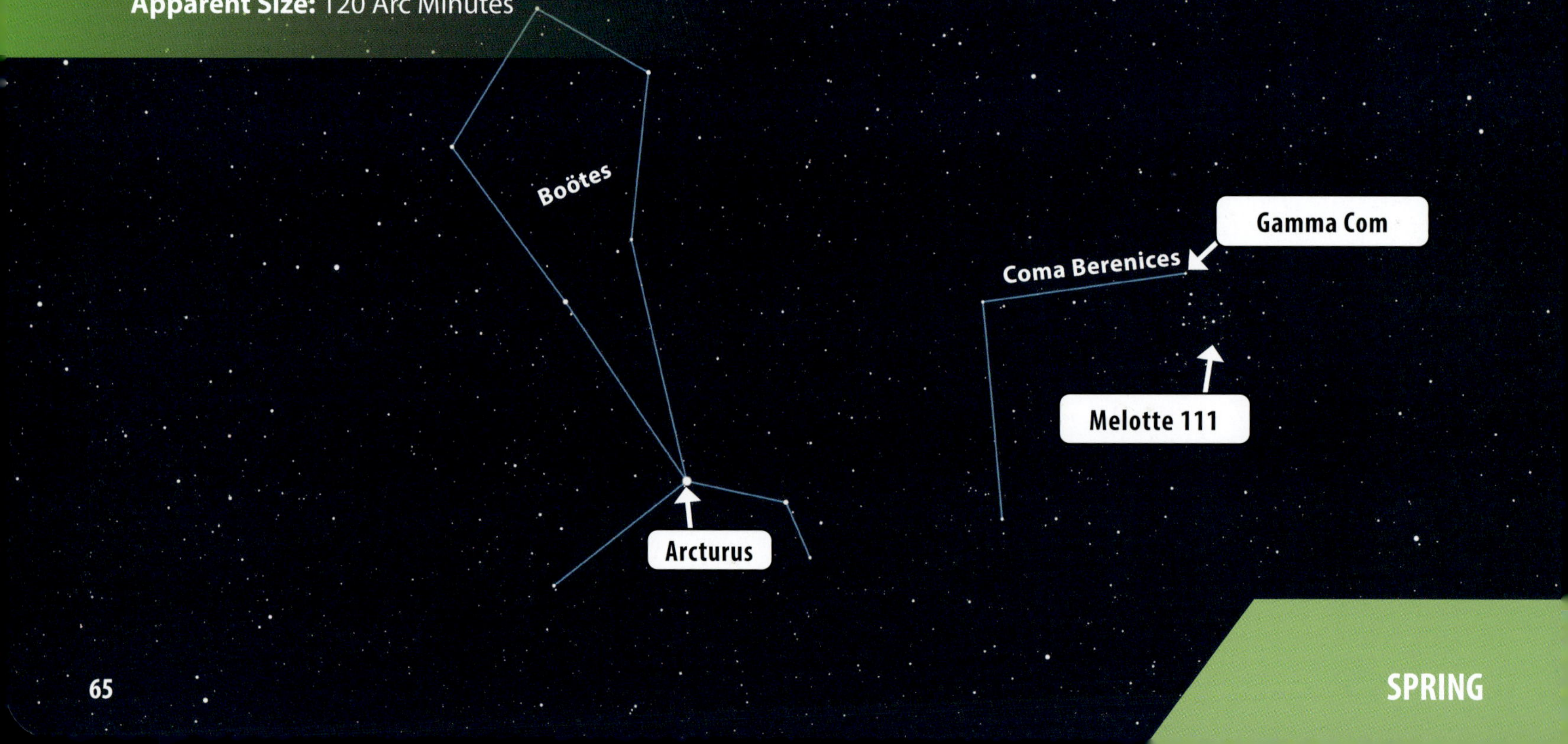

SPRING

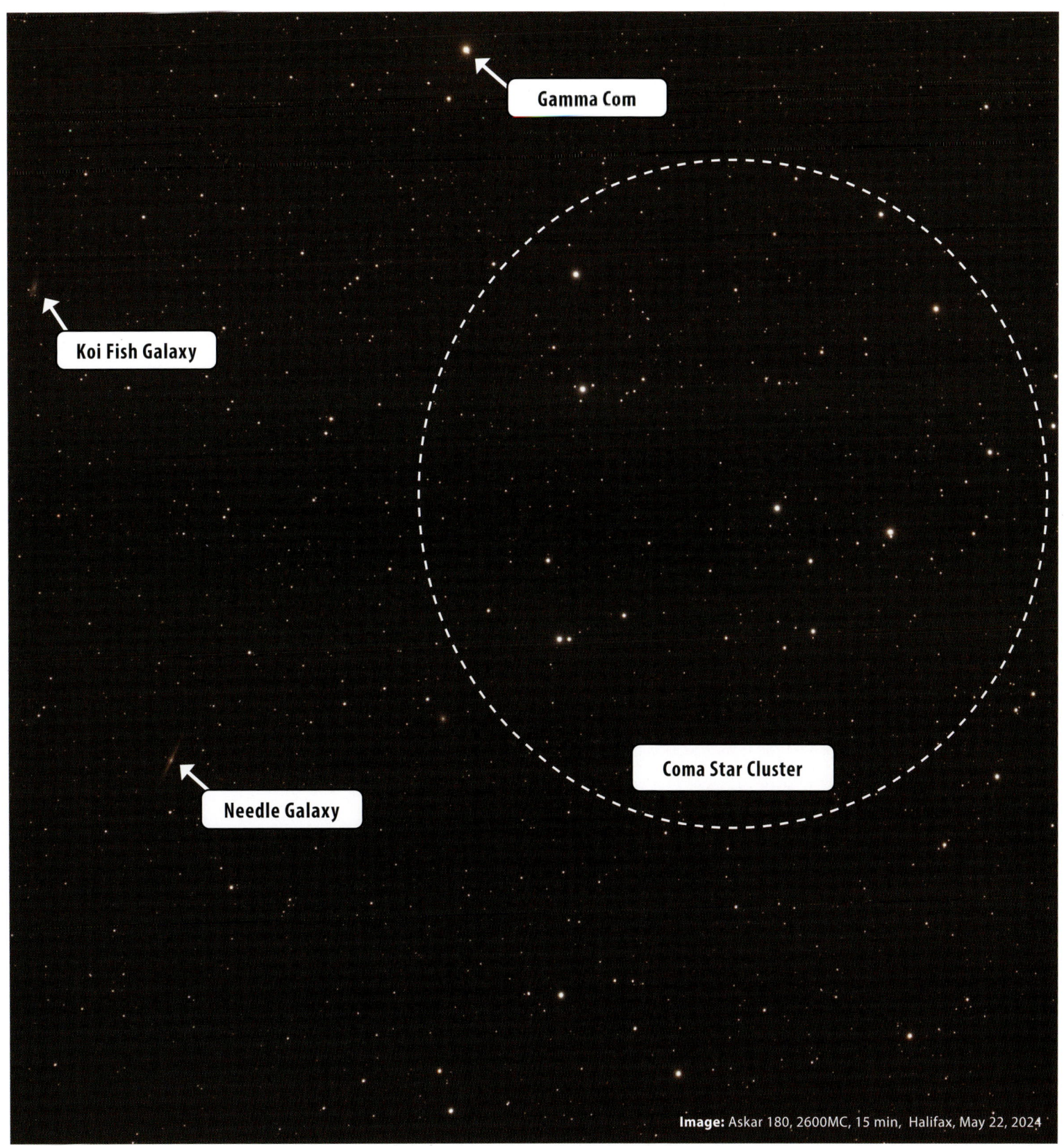

Image: Askar 180, 2600MC, 15 min, Halifax, May 22, 2024

41. The Galaxies of Leo

Although springtime is known as the "galaxy" season in the astronomy community, for binocular observers, viewing galaxies in spring can be a bit of a bust. However, if you happen to find yourself under pitch-black skies during spring, here are a few galaxies to start off your search.

The first one is NGC 2903, which I'm calling the "Forgotten Galaxy" because I'm sure Charles Messier must have come across it during one of his comet hunts. This is one of the largest and brightest galaxies that is NOT on Charles Messier's famous list. It's also relatively easy to find, assuming your skies are VERY dark. You'll locate it just off the tip of the Sickle in Leo, and it's for this reason that astronomer Chris Vaughan calls it the "Lion's Tongue."

The second is the Trio in Leo. Though sometimes when I view this, I'm only able to make out M65 and M66. NGC 3628 (a.k.a. the "Hamburger") always seems just out of reach.

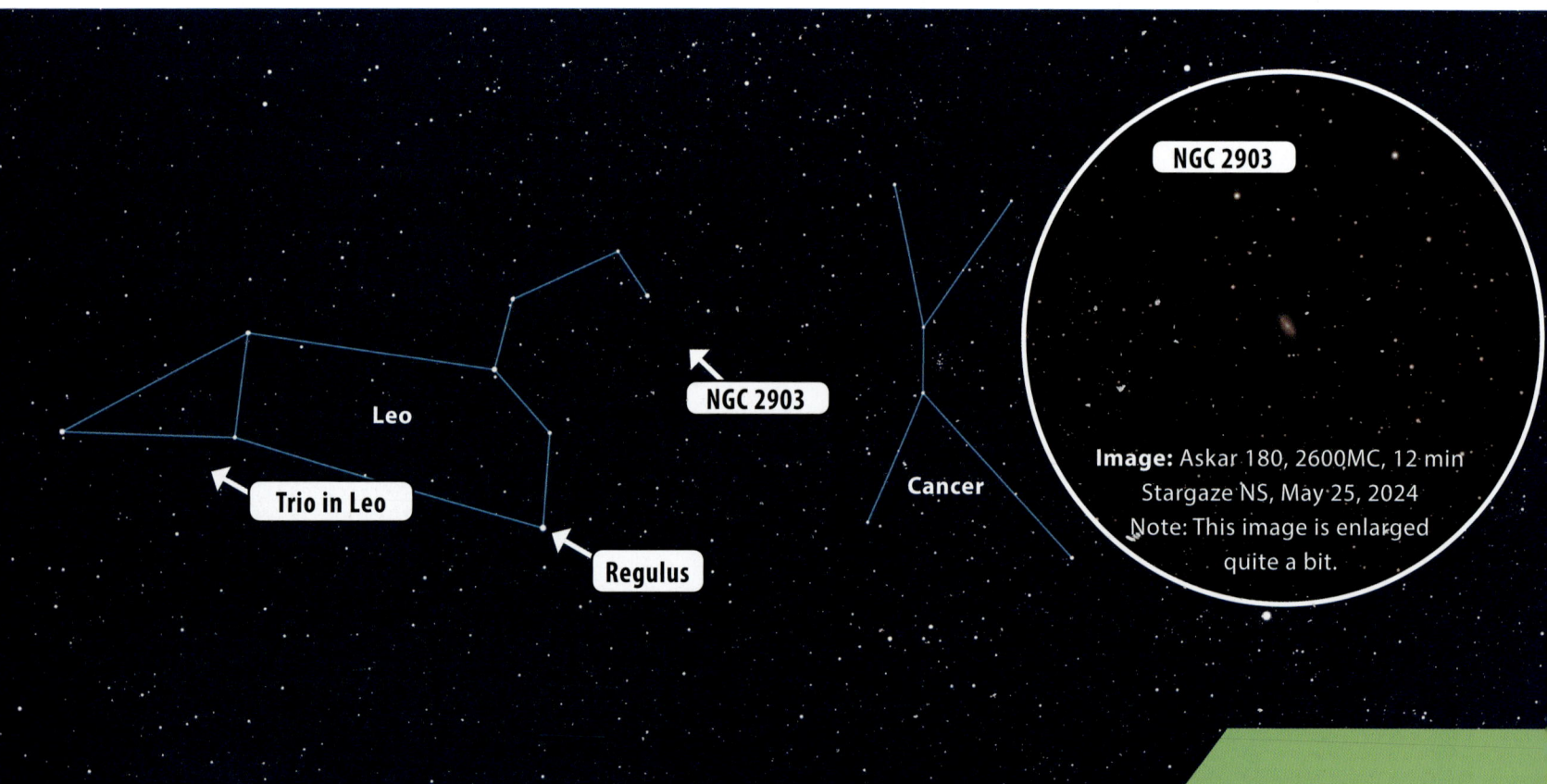

Image: Askar 180, 2600MC, 12 min
Stargaze NS, May 25, 2024
Note: This image is enlarged quite a bit.

SPRING

Object of Interest: M66
Dark Sky Requirement: VERY dark skies
Object Type: Spiral Galaxy
Brightness: 8.9
Distance: 37 Million Light-Years
Apparent Size: 10.3 x 4.6 Arc Minutes

Hamburger Galaxy

M65

M66

Image: Askar 180, 2600MC, 6 min, Biosphere 2 (Arizona), May 10, 2024

42. Spring Double Stars

Spring is the busiest season for double stars, at least in RASC's "Explore the Universe" program, which contains ten double stars, the same number as all other seasons combined. (Note that some of these were covered in the circumpolar section.)

There are many more springtime double stars listed in the Astronomical League binocular program;[1] however, I found many of these to be too difficult to observe with 7x50s. That said, be sure to check out these programs; this way, you can earn certificates for your observations. Be sure to use the additional sketching circles located in the rear of this book.

---

[1] www.astroleague.org/binocular-double-star-observing-program

OBSERVING LOG

Date: Time: Location:

Sky Conditions (Seeing/Transparency):

Instrument (Magnification/Aperture):

Notes:

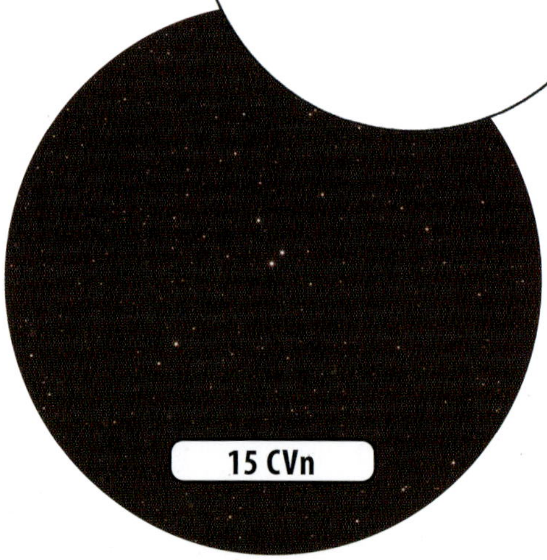

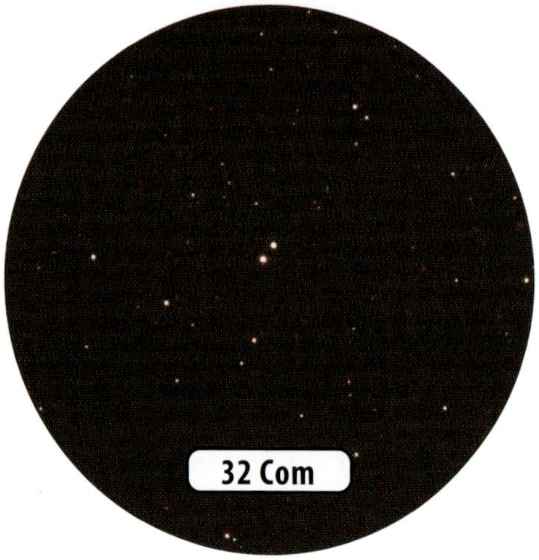

- Mu Boo
- Delta Boo
- 15 CVn
- Adhafera
- 32 Com
- Zubenelgenubi II

SPRING

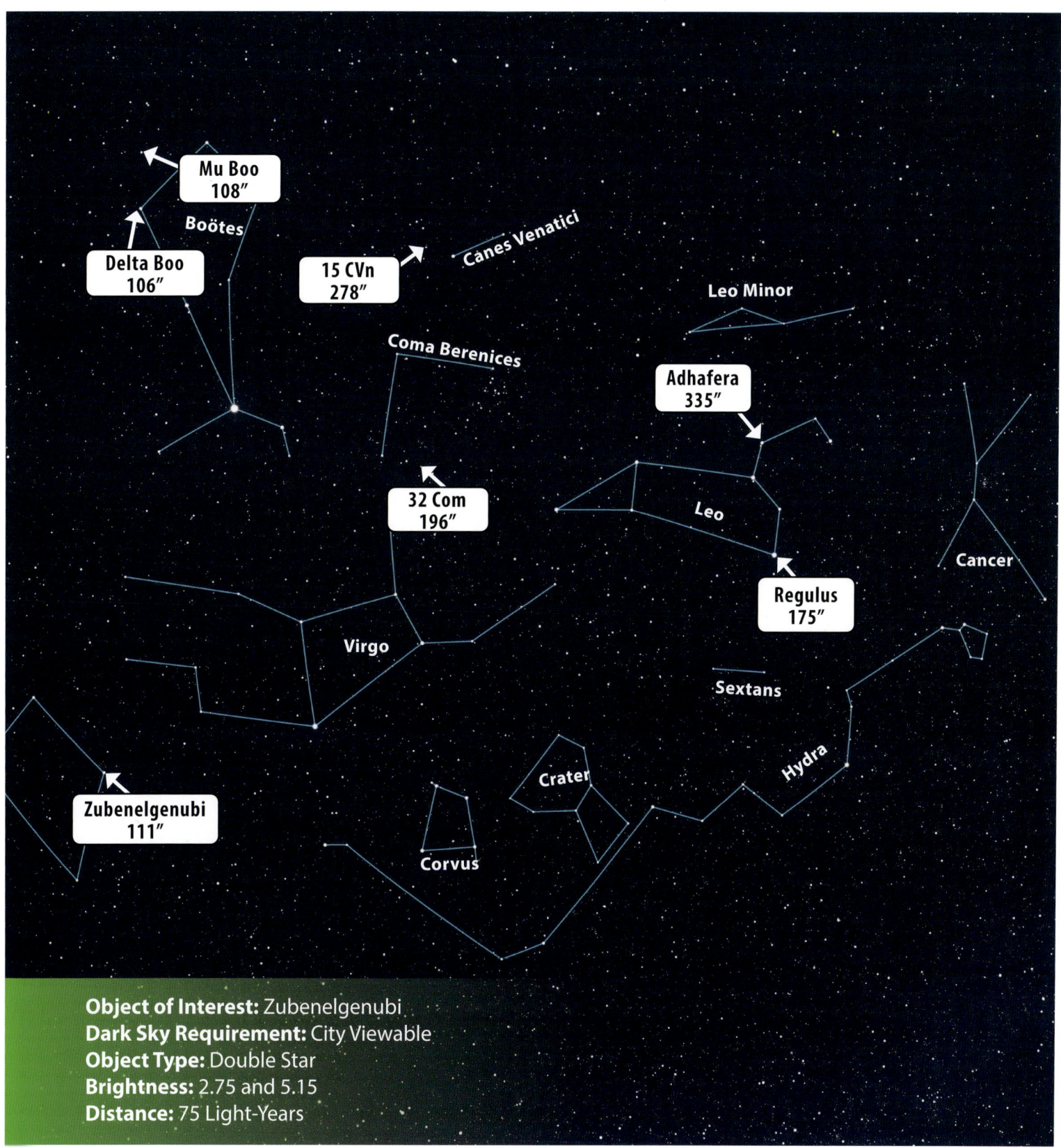

Object of Interest: Zubenelgenubi
Dark Sky Requirement: City Viewable
Object Type: Double Star
Brightness: 2.75 and 5.15
Distance: 75 Light-Years

SOLAR SYSTEM OBJECTS AND EVENTS

Many stargazing books ignore the Moon and planets as potential targets for stargazing. I believe that observing the Moon, planets, and other objects, including fun challenges like lunar occultations, should be part of an observer's regular routine.

For example, during a conjunction, it can be quite fun to get two celestial objects in the same field of view at the same time. During the conjunction of Jupiter and Saturn in December of 2020, dozens of people braved the cold (and the pandemic) to observe these two planets in the same field of view through my telescope.

Given the much larger field of view of binoculars, two-in-one views of celestial objects are quite frequent! For example, on August 5, 2024, a few minutes after sunset, you might have been able to get Venus, a sliver of the Moon, and the bright star Regulus in the same field of view, just moments before they set below the horizon—a fun challenge for the dedicated observer!

Most of these events will be forecasted on astronomy websites, in magazines, and during "what's up" sessions at astronomy clubs. But you don't have to wait; you can use astronomy software, run it forward in time, and forecast these events all on your own!

There are several solar system events that do not require binoculars (or a telescope) to observe. Meteor showers are best observed without binoculars, since you want to be paying attention to as much sky as possible to maximize your chances of seeing a meteor. Lunar eclipses do not require binoculars, although the experience may be more interesting if you do use them. We'll talk more about meteor showers and lunar eclipses on the next page.

Sometimes, comets become so bright that they can be seen without binoculars from dark skies. Total solar eclipses are also best observed without any gear, although you will require eclipse glasses for the partial phases.

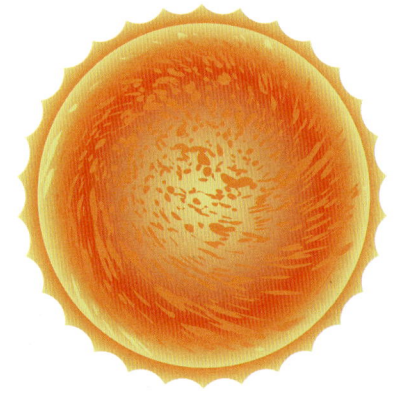
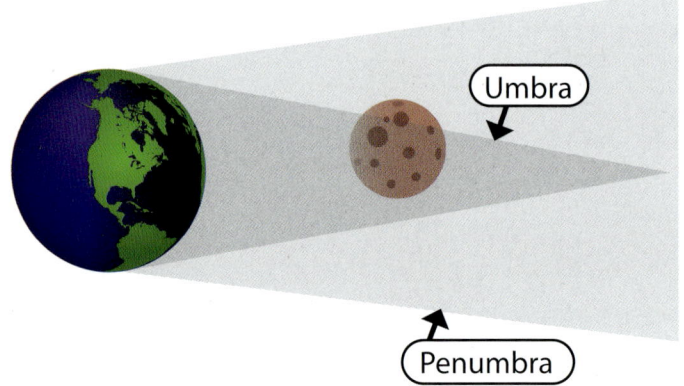

How lunar eclipses work

BINOCULARS OPTIONAL

Lunar Eclipses

Lunar eclipses only occur during the full Moon. Lunar eclipses occur on average a couple of times per year. However, some years there are none. Depending on where you live on Earth, a lunar eclipse may occur before moonrise, or after moonset from your location. To determine the time of the next lunar eclipse, it's best to look it up online.

Why don't lunar eclipses occur every month? The Moon's orbit is inclined versus the Earth's orbit around the Sun. When the Moon passes the plane of the Earth's orbit, we call this a "node." Eclipses only occur when the full Moon is near a node.

Meteor Showers

Meteor showers occur several times per year, but some are more impressive then others. For example, the Perseids (mid-August) and the Geminids (December) have reputations for being the most impressive. Often, until the event peaks, it's hard to know if that particular meteor shower is going to be a good one.

Some tips for viewing meteor showers:

- Stay up late. Meteor showers tend to get better after midnight.
- Find dark skies. Light pollution hides all but the brightest meteors. From dark skies, you may see a meteor every thirty seconds or so.
- Adjust your eyes to the dark by avoiding artificial light sources, including camera and phone screens.
- Choose a night near the peak where the Moon will not be in the sky during the times you plan to observe.
- Don't worry about looking in a particular direction. Just sit back and take in as much sky as possible.
- Dress warm, and bring friends. Meteor showers can be quite exciting!

Image: Canon T3i, Focal Length 50mm, 0.25 sec exp, Halifax, Nova Scotia, November 8, 2022

Image: Geminid from Stargaze Nova Scotia. Sony A7s, Focal Length 28mm, 20 sec exp, December 14, 2023

43. Conjunctions and Occultations

For stargazing purposes, a conjunction is any time objects appear together in the night sky. For example, the Moon, over the course of its twenty-seven-day orbit, will have a conjunction with every planet in the solar system. That doesn't mean all of these conjunctions will be noteworthy, but some will. Sometimes you get a grouping of three objects together, such as the Moon, Jupiter, and Venus. When that happens, it's worth gathering your friends and having a bit of a star party. Conjunctions make a good excuse to gather people together to appreciate the night sky.

Occultations occur when the planets (or bright stars) appear to pass behind the Moon. These can be a bit more challenging to observe since the observations are often brief, lasting only a few hours, and they are only visible from certain locations on Earth. For example, while an occultation of Jupiter by the Moon may be visible from South America, stargazers in North America may only witness a conjunction. Jupiter would simply pass near the Moon without going behind it.

OBSERVING LOG

Date: Time: Location:

Sky Conditions (Seeing/Transparency):

Instrument (Magnification/Aperture):

Notes:

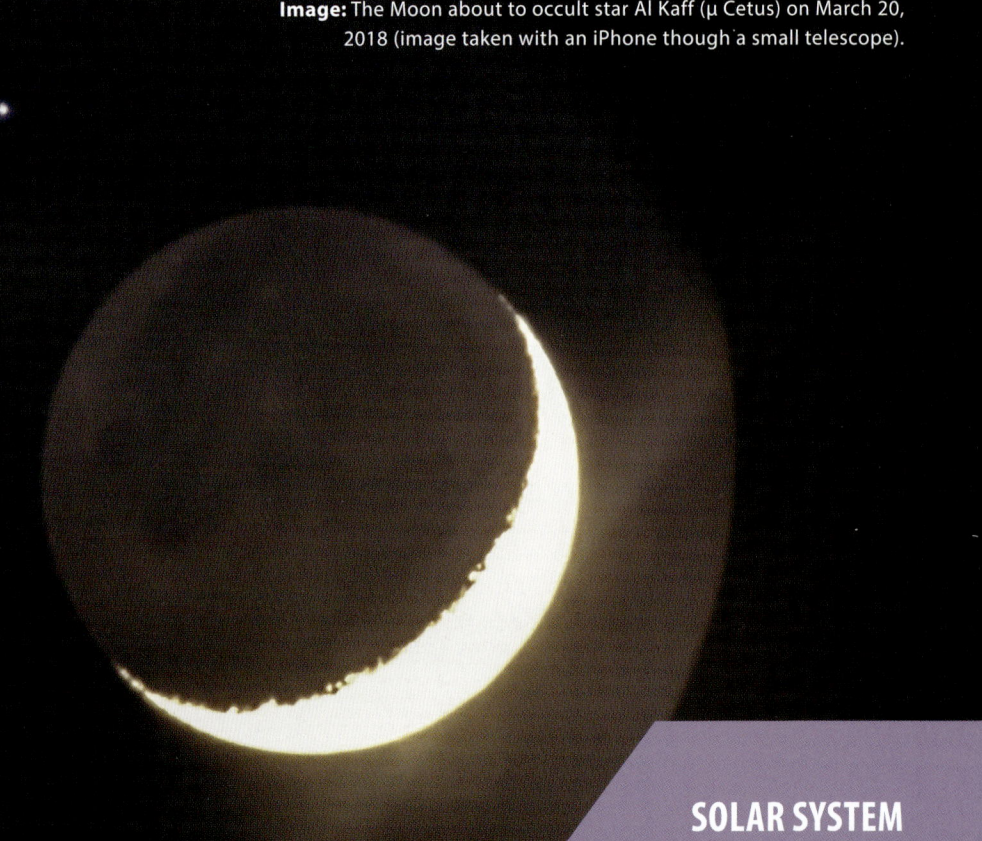

Image: The Moon about to occult star Al Kaff (μ Cetus) on March 20, 2018 (image taken with an iPhone though a small telescope).

SOLAR SYSTEM

44. Full Moon and the Lunar Seas

When the Moon is full or nearly full, you should be able to identify all the major lunar seas in any pair of binoculars. The "seas" are in fact large lava plains that were formed after impacts of asteroids.

In 7x50 binoculars, the Moon won't take up much of your field of view. Sometimes, the Moon looks huge as it rises (this is known as the Moon illusion), but through the binoculars, you could still fit ten full moons (or more) across your binoculars' field of view.

The full Moon is also a good time to view rayed craters like Tycho. These are more recent craters (only a few hundred million years old) whose ejecta are visible in white bands that stretch almost across an entire hemisphere of the Moon's surface.

Although the Moon may appear small in the image below, your eyes are fully capable of taking in an incredible amount of detail. Steadiness is key, however, and having a tripod or monopod will vastly increase your ability to concentrate on the finer details.

OBSERVING LOG

Date:　　　　　Time:　　　　　Location:

Sky Conditions (Seeing/Transparency):

Instrument (Magnification/Aperture):

Notes:

"Ray" Craters that should be visible in binoculars during the full Moon.

About how the Moon will appear in binoculars (Stellarium)

SOLAR SYSTEM

Object of Interest: Full Moon
Dark Sky Requirement: City Viewable
Brightness: −12.7 (only when full)
Distance: 384,400 km (on average)
Apparent Size: ~30 Arc Minutes

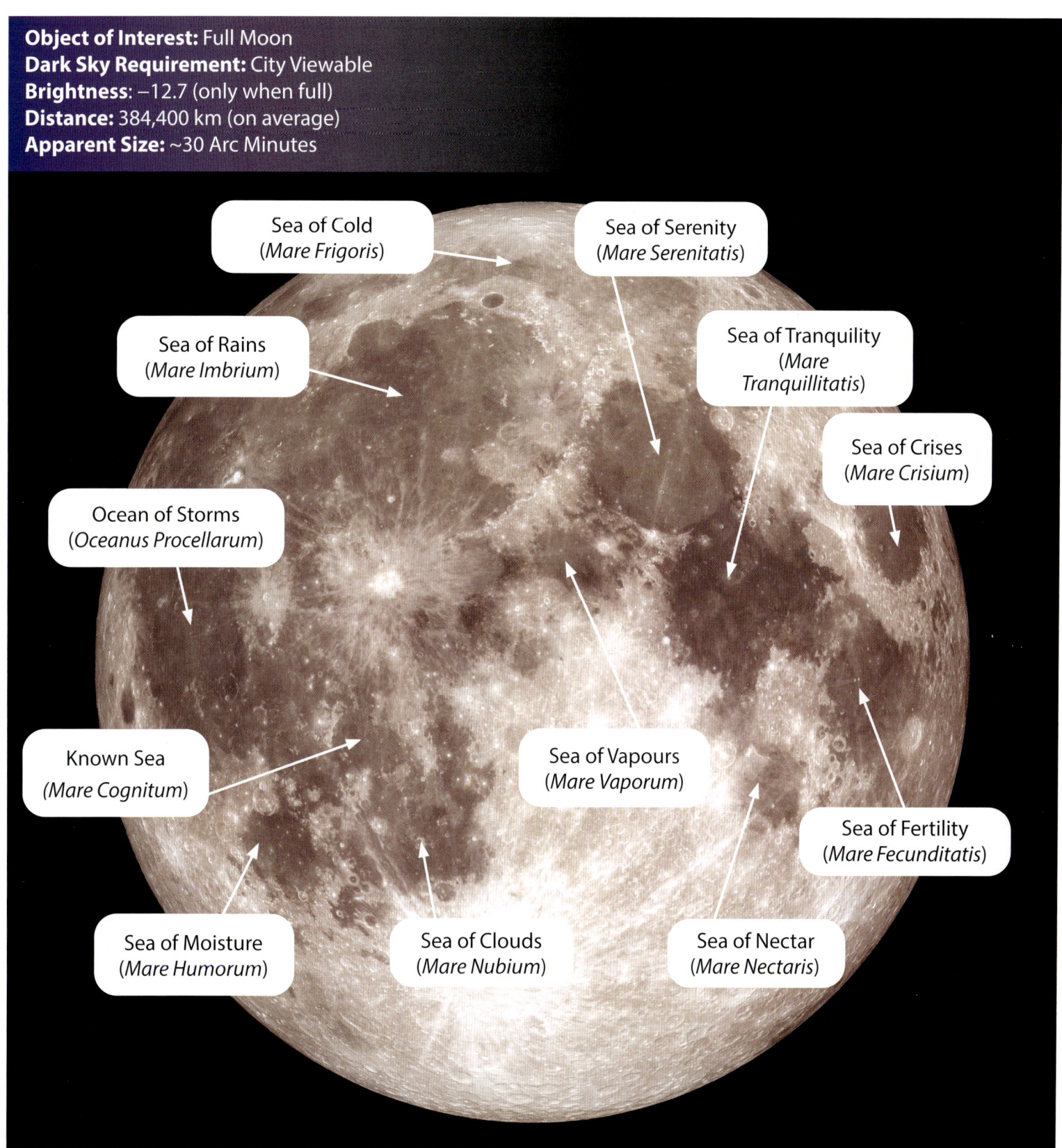

45. Lunar Phases and Big Craters

As the Moon orbits around the Earth, it passes through "phases." These phases repeat every 29 days. The Moon is only in the evening sky from the young crescent phase (a few days after the new Moon) until the full Moon, about 12 days later. After the full Moon, the Moon rises later and later each night. For the purpose of this book, I assume you're observing in the evening, so we will ignore the phases after the full Moon.

Typically, when observing the Moon through binoculars, the craters that will be most prominent are those located near the "terminator," which is the line between the daytime and nighttime sides of the Moon. Here are a few features to look for during these phases:

Young Moon: When the Moon is just a thin sliver, look for four large craters running along the terminator (the line between lunar night and day). These are nicknamed the "Gang of Four" (from top to bottom: Langrenus, Vendelinus, Petavius, and Furnerius).

Crescent Moon: Now there are many craters visible; the most easily identifiable are Cleomedes on the shore of the Sea of Crises, and Posidonius, a smooth-floored crater on the shore of the Sea of Serenity.

First Quarter: Look for the Apennine Mountains. Many big and bright craters can be observed along the terminator. Sunlit features, like the dumbbell craters (Cyrillus and Catharina), are also visible.

"Young" Gibbous: Shortly after the first Quarter, prominent craters such as Plato, Copernicus, and Clavius appear.

Gibbous: During this phase, Sinus Iridum ("Bay of Rainbows") is clearly visible, as is Gassendi (which looks like a diamond ring at higher magnifications).

"Nearly" Full: When the Moon is almost full, look for the small but bright crater Aristarchus, and two giant craters, Grimaldi, and Schickard.

OBSERVING LOG

Date:	Time:	Location:

Sky Conditions (Seeing/Transparency):

Instrument (Magnification/Aperture):

Notes:

Use the sketching circles located in the rear of this book.

After the full Moon, the Moon rises later and later in the evening and into the morning. These phases, where the Moon goes from full Moon to new Moon, are called the "waning" phases. Since I mainly stargaze in the hours after sunset (and not in the morning), I seldom encounter these phases.

The Moon at sunset as it approaches first quarter. Captured via iPhone in my 20x70 tripod-mounted binoculars.

SOLAR SYSTEM

Waxing Lunar Phases

Young Moon. During this phase, the Moon is very low in the sky and sets soon after sunset.

Crescent. During this phase, the Moon sets within a few hours of sunset.

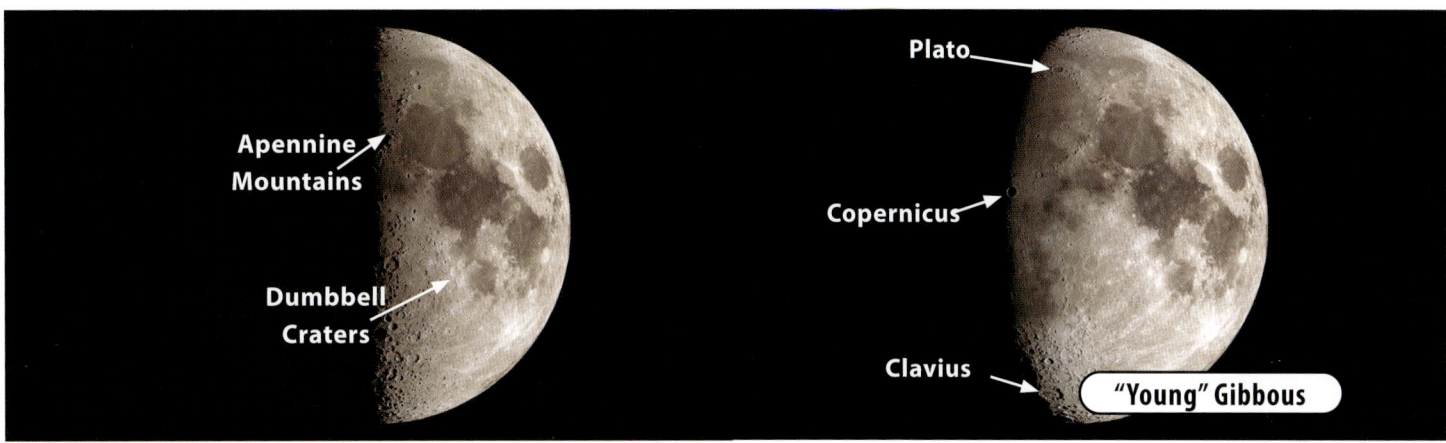

First Quarter. During this phase, the Moon rises around noon (yes, you can see it during the day) and sets at midnight.

(Young) Gibbous. After first quarter, the Moon rises in the afternoon, and stays in the sky late into the night.

The Gibbous Moon is nearly full, and in the sky most of the night. Most of the lunar seas are visible.

The "Nearly" full Moon is in the sky most of the night. All the lunar seas are now visible.

46. Jupiter and Its Moons

Observing Jupiter's moons with binoculars is a testament to how amazing binoculars are as an invention. We think of binoculars as simple instruments, more commonplace than the telescope itself.

Before the invention of the telescope in 1609, no one in history had ever observed Jupiter's moons. The fact that you can make this observation with simple binoculars is a profound statement that we are truly in a modern age.

Three of the moons, Io, Europa, and Ganymede, are found close to Jupiter, while Callisto is generally observed a bit farther away. Astronomy magazines often contain a prediction of the positions of the Galilean moons in the form of a helical diagram. In the diagram, the orange, yellow, and red lines represent Io, Europa, and Ganymede, respectively, while the blue line represents Callisto. Note that Jupiter has seventy-nine moons in total, but only these four are visible in binoculars and small telescopes.

Jupiter's moon locations are predictable and can be read like a clock. In fact, in many instances in history, before the age of instantaneous communication, these moons were used to synchronize clocks so that astronomical observations could be carried out simultaneously across the globe.

Object of Interest: Jupiter (and its moons)
Dark Sky Requirement: City Viewable
Object Type: Planet (Gas Giant)
Brightness: −2.9 (dimmest), −1.7 (brightest)
Distance: 778 million km (from the Sun)
Apparent Size: ~40 Arc Seconds

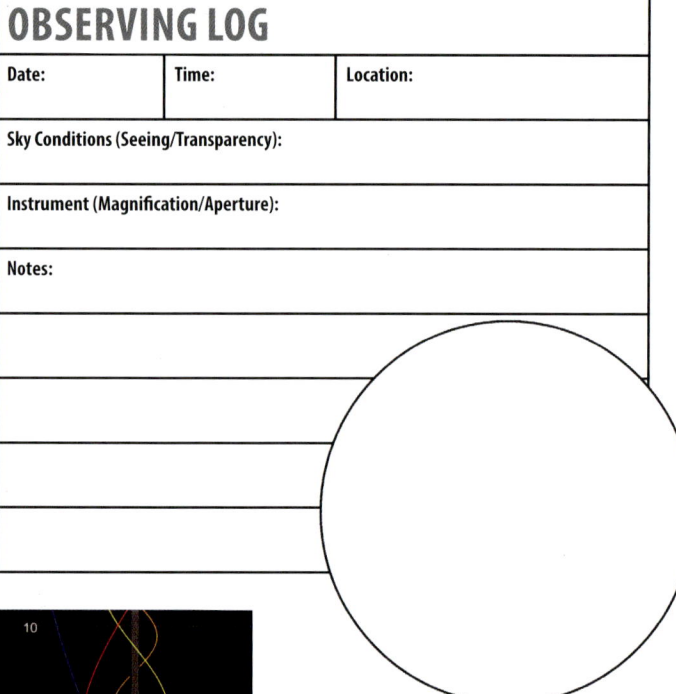

OBSERVING LOG
Date: Time: Location:
Sky Conditions (Seeing/Transparency):
Instrument (Magnification/Aperture):
Notes:

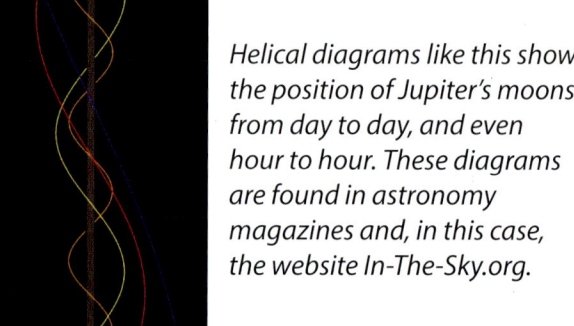

Helical diagrams like this show the position of Jupiter's moons from day to day, and even hour to hour. These diagrams are found in astronomy magazines and, in this case, the website In-The-Sky.org.

Jupiter as it would appear in binoculars

Jupiter imaged by the Hubble Space Telescope

SOLAR SYSTEM

47. Venus and Its Phases

With steady hands or with the aid of a monopod or tripod, Venus will often appear as more than a bright point of light. For binocular observers, it will often appear as a tiny version of our Moon. Venus has phases, depending on its position relative to the Earth and Sun. Sometimes Venus appears as a crescent, sometimes it's half illuminated, like a first quarter moon, and other times, it's gibbous or almost round. The phases of Venus are another of Galileo's great discoveries.

You shouldn't wait until dark to observe Venus. In fact, catching it just after sunset is best, as the contrast from the bright sky will help you better observe the current phase. Venus orbits between the Earth and the Sun, so from our perspective, it never stays very far from the Sun. Venus either appears just after sunset, setting soon after, or just before sunrise. It can even be viewed during the day, and even without a telescope or binoculars, but only if you know exactly where to look.

Object of Interest: Venus
Dark Sky Requirement: City Viewable
Object Type: Planet
Brightness: −4.92 (dimmest) to −2.98 (brightest)
Distance: ~108 million km from the Sun
Apparent Size: 9.9 to 68 Arc Seconds (a massive swing)

Venus captured with the author's 90mm telescope

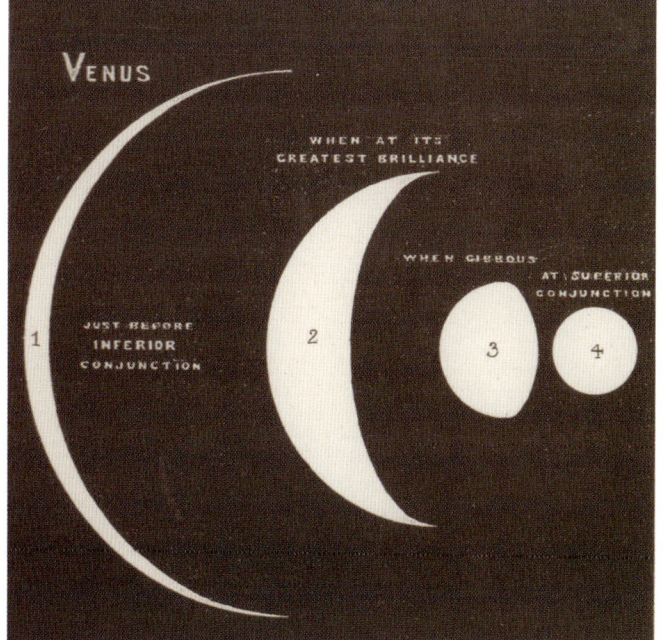

Description and drawing of Venus's phases from An Atlas of Astronomy by Sir Robert Ball 1889

SOLAR SYSTEM

48. The "Other" Planets

Finding planets through binoculars can be a fun challenge, even if the planets don't appear any brighter than an average star within your field of view. Note that planets move from night to night, so you'll need astronomy software to plot their location.

Mars will appear as a very bright red dot, and Saturn as a very bright yellow dot. High-aperture binoculars on tripods will show Saturn's rings. Uranus and Neptune will appear as small bluish stars.

I've added minor planet (asteroid) Vesta to this list because it is typically slightly brighter than Neptune.

Mercury is bright but still challenging to observe. This planet is only possible to view for a week or so, several times each year. And on these nights, it's only visible for a few minutes after sunset or before sunrise. And then there is dwarf planet Ceres and minor planet Vesta, which can be as bright as a dim star but challenging to distinguish from background stars. No, you're not going to see Pluto, sorry.

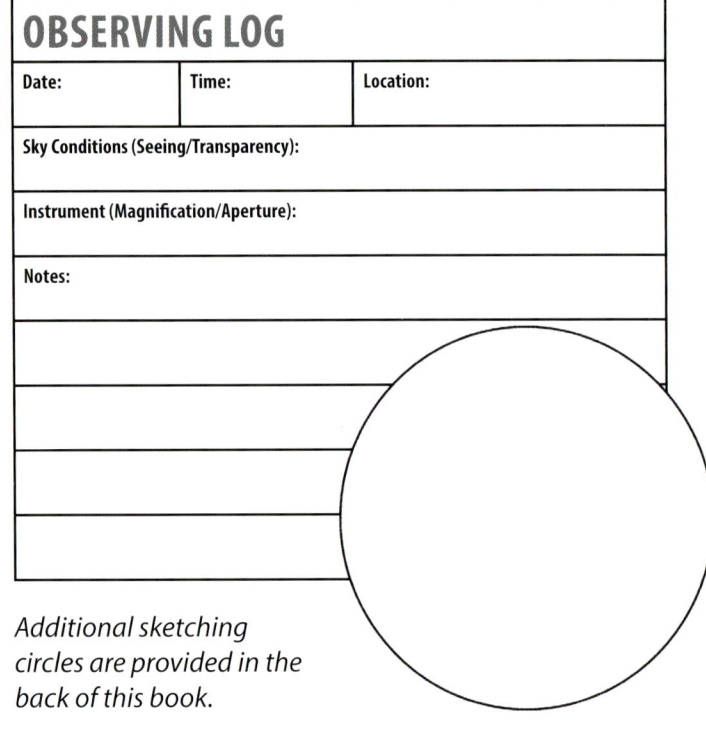

Additional sketching circles are provided in the back of this book.

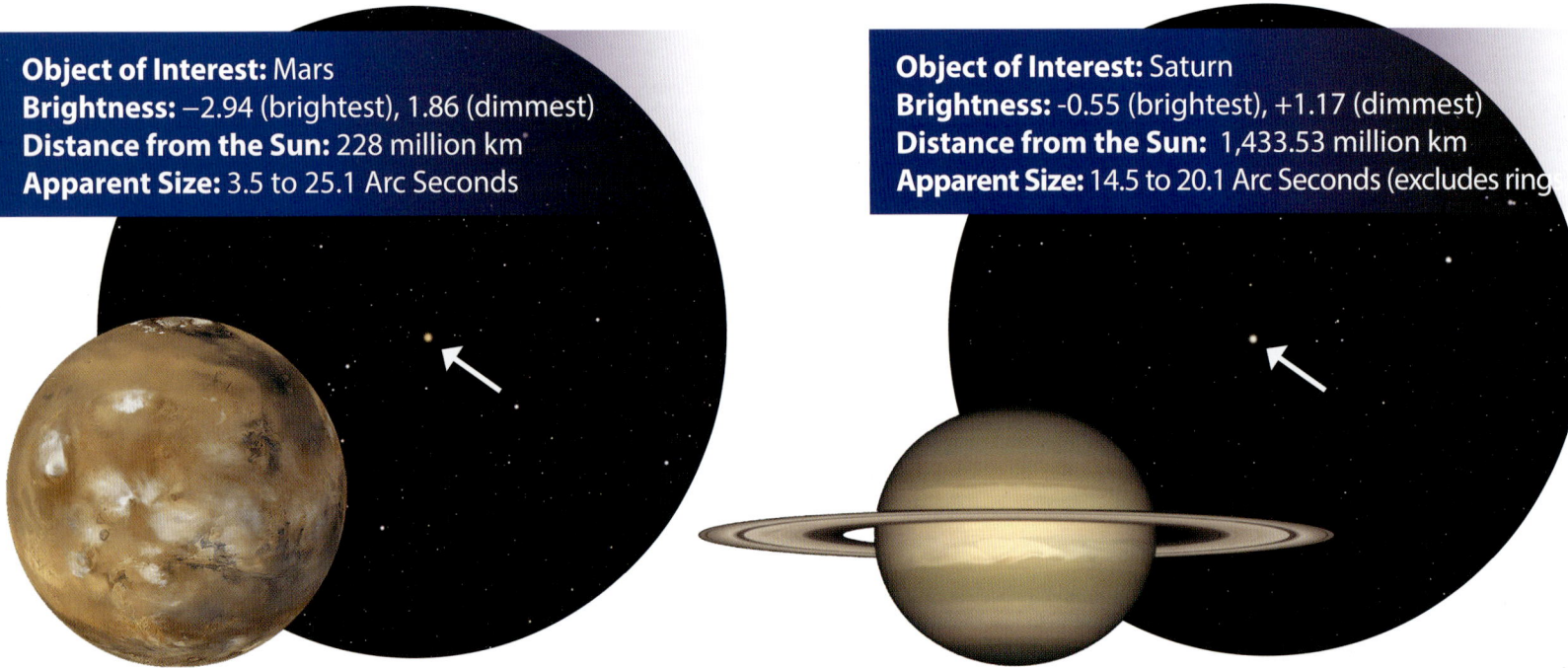

Object of Interest: Mars
Brightness: −2.94 (brightest), 1.86 (dimmest)
Distance from the Sun: 228 million km
Apparent Size: 3.5 to 25.1 Arc Seconds

Composite image of Mars by the Mars Reconnaissance Orbiter (MRO) spacecraft

Object of Interest: Saturn
Brightness: -0.55 (brightest), +1.17 (dimmest)
Distance from the Sun: 1,433.53 million km
Apparent Size: 14.5 to 20.1 Arc Seconds (excludes rings)

Saturn imaged by the Cassini spacecraft

SOLAR SYSTEM

Object of Interest: Mercury
Brightness: −2.48 (brightest) to +7.25 (dimmest)
Distance from the Sun: 57.91 million km
Apparent Size: 4.5–13.0 Arc Seconds

Mercury imaged in representative color by the MESSENGER spacecraft

Object of Interest: Asteroid Vesta
Brightness: 5.1 (brightest) to 8.5 (dimmest)
Distance from the Sun: 353 million km
Apparent Size: Point Source

Asteroid Vesta, imaged by the Dawn spacecraft. This asteroid is visible in binoculars as a small point of light.

Object of Interest: Uranus
Brightness: About 5.7
Distance from the Sun: 2.9 billion km
Apparent Size: 3.3 to 4.1 Arc Seconds

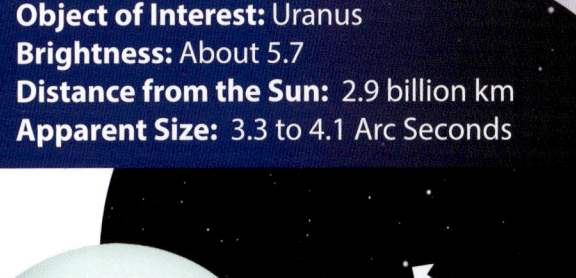

Uranus imaged by the Voyager 2 spacecraft

*Binocular views of the planets simulated in Stellarium.

Object of Interest: Neptune
Brightness: About 7.8
Distance from the Sun: 4.50 billion km
Apparent Size: About 2.3 Arc Seconds

Neptune imaged by the Voyager 2 spacecraft

49. Comets

Comets are city-sized conglomerations of ice and dirty rock that orbit the Sun with periods so long that they often only spend a minuscule fraction of their time closer to the Sun than Jupiter. When they get within a few hundred million miles of the Sun (that's close!), the Sun's radiation and solar wind start eating away at the surface of the comet, leaving a trail of gas and dust millions of kilometers long and thousands of kilometers wide. Within a month or so, the comet's trajectory takes it away from the Sun, in most cases, for hundreds or thousands of years.

It was during the appearance of the comet C/2020 F3 (NEOWISE) in 2020 that I first looked at a comet with regular binoculars (I'd used astronomy binoculars on previous comets). This happened in the summer of 2020. I was setting up some camera gear on top of Citadel Hill in Halifax, Nova Scotia, with Tiffany Fields, my colleague at the Burke-Gaffney Observatory. We just happened to have brought an old pair of binoculars, and after exposing the comet just after sunset with a camera (image below), we were able to pinpoint exactly where to point the binoculars, bringing the comet into view.

Comets can be tricky targets. The media often hypes them up as a big event, as if you'll see a giant colorful light show streaking across the sky. In reality, comets often break apart and effectively fizzle out before they even become bright enough to see with a telescope.

I've added instructions in the appendix of this book to help you add recently discovered comets to Stellarium (free stargazing software). Sometimes the charts you'll find on the Internet aren't very helpful, and it's far easier to make your own.

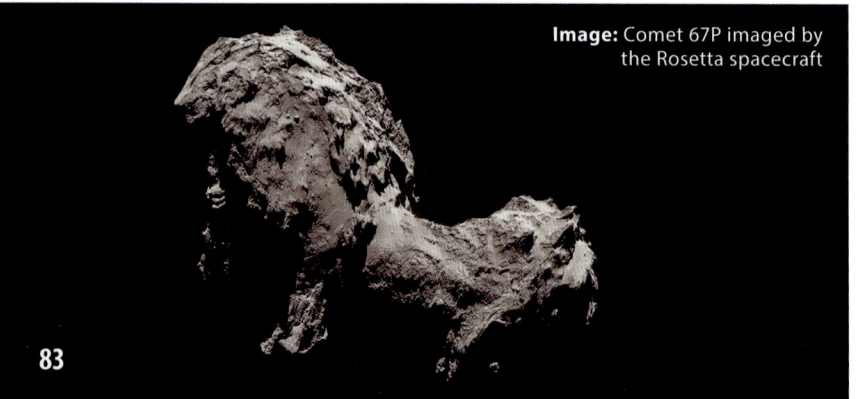

Image: Comet 67P imaged by the Rosetta spacecraft

OBSERVING LOG

Date: Time: Location:

Sky Conditions (Seeing/Transparency):

Instrument (Magnification/Aperture):

Notes:

Comet Neowise

SOLAR SYSTEM

Object of Interest: Comet
Dark Sky Requirement: Darker the Better
Brightness: Varies
Distance: Generally under 100 million km

Image: Comet PANSTARRS viewed from Concord, California. The image was taken with a telephoto lens. The comet looked just like this through my 20x70 astronomy binoculars.

50. Solar Observing

I actually began my journey in binocular astronomy with solar observing. Before I even pointed my astronomy binoculars at the stars, I had them fitted with solar filters made of Baader film and used them to observe the 2012 transit of Venus. Only later did I use them for observing sunspots.

Sunspots are magnetic storms on the surface of the Sun. Flares, brief, bright bursts of light and X-rays, often emanate from these spots. These flares are often followed by a coronal mass ejection (CME) which, if directed at the Earth, coincides with the appearance of the northern lights at high latitudes.

As with observing the Moon, you can see a lot more detail in the sunspots if you stabilize the binoculars with a tripod. In mosts cases, the sun will look white through filtered binoculars, but it could appear to be different colors depending on the sky conditions. For example, it may appear more orange near sunset, or during forest fire season, like when I started writing this book.

Around the time of the 2017 eclipse of the Sun, I purchased a pair of 10x42 Eclipse-Smart solar binoculars. These are great because you can instantly check out the current count of large sunspots. During the April 8, 2024, eclipse, I saw several people using regular binoculars to view the solar eclipse at totality, when the Moon fully covers the Sun, and it is safe to look at unfiltered. This is a bit risky for my taste, but it must have been an amazing sight. The bottom right solar image shows an unfiltered view of the total solar eclipse (at totality).

10x42 Eclipse-Smart Binoculars

OBSERVING LOG

Date: Time: Location:

Sky Conditions (Seeing/Transparency):

Instrument (Magnification/Aperture):

Notes:

Sun Spots

Warning! Pointing unfiltered binoculars at the Sun will cause permanent eye damage.

Image: Seestar S50, Doaktown, New Brunswick, April 8, 2024

SOLAR SYSTEM

Object of Interest: The Sun
Gear Requirement: Solar Filters
Object Type: G-Type Star
Brightness: −26.7
Distance: ~149 million km
Apparent Size: 30 Arc Minutes

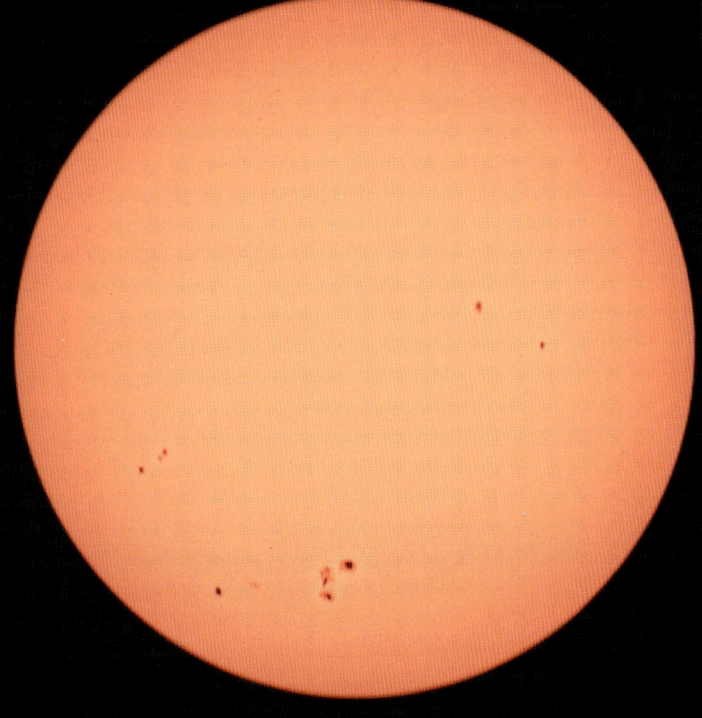

Image: Seestar S50, Focal Length 250mm, Aperture 50mm, best 69 exps of a 4-second video, Halifax, Nova Scotia, Stella helping (me take this photo).

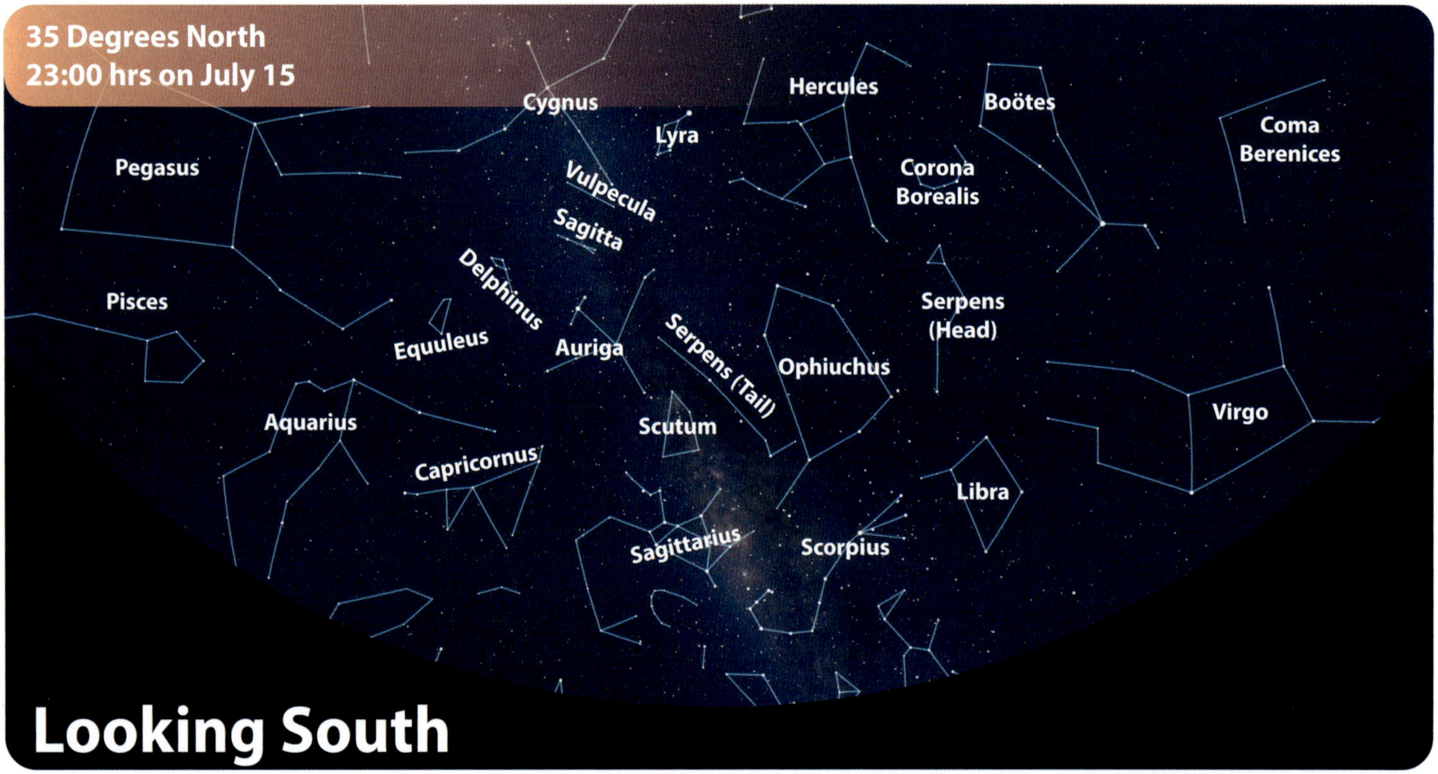

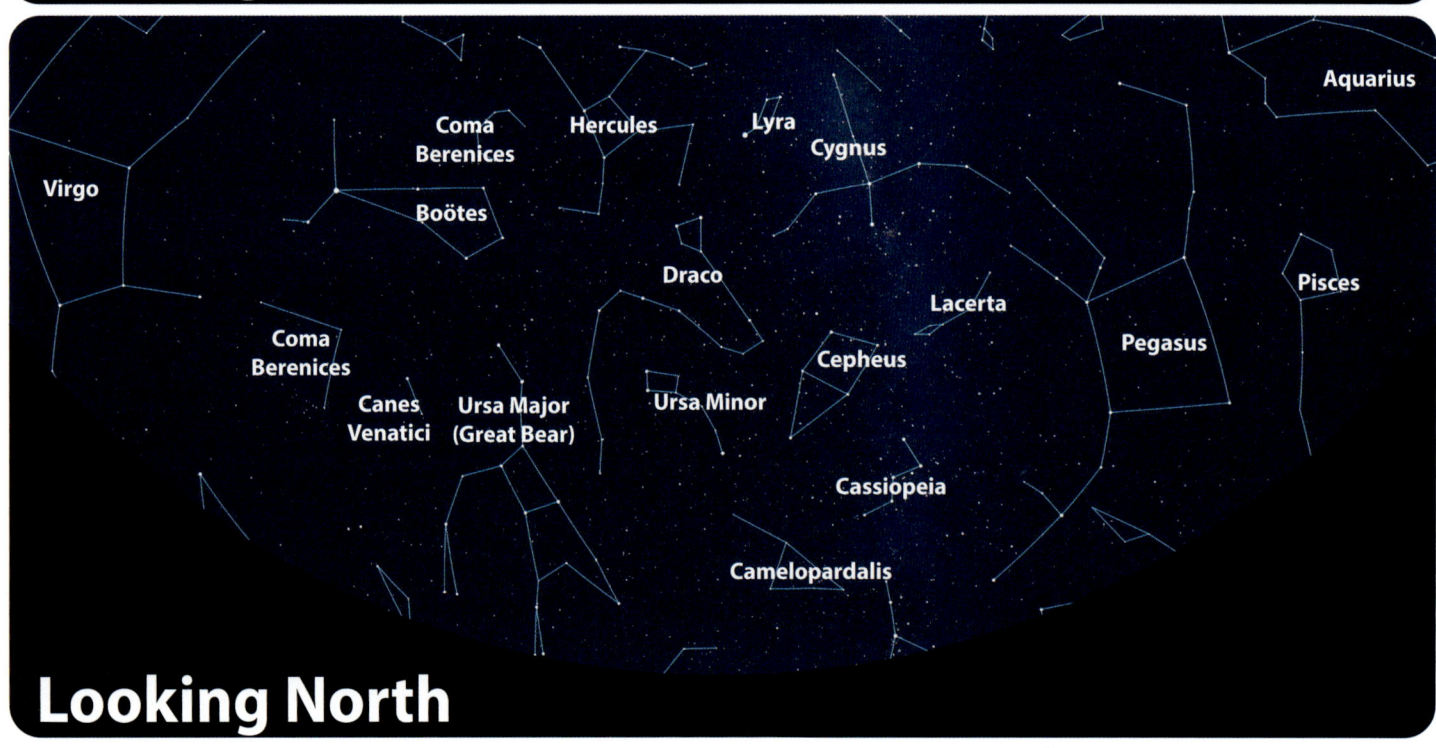

Autumn Full-Sky Constellations

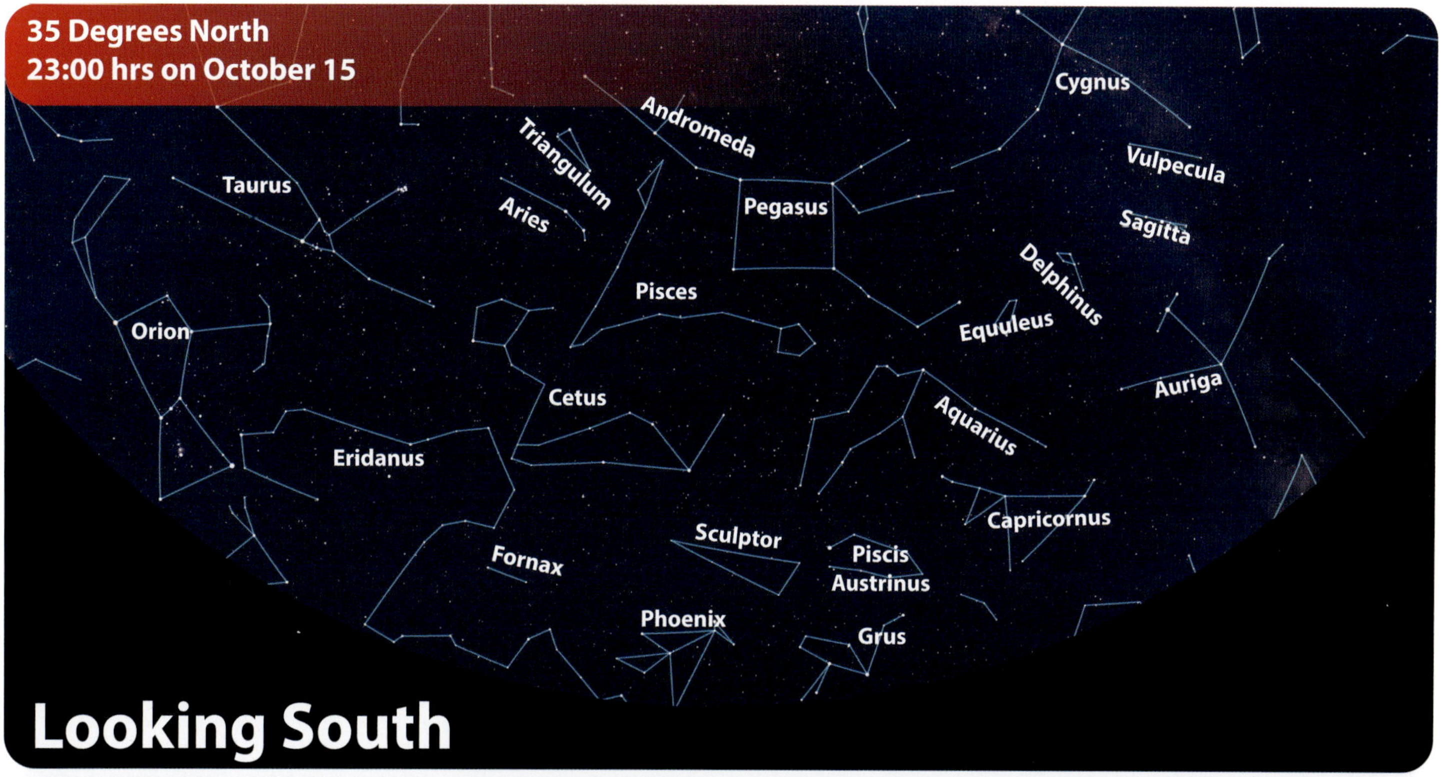

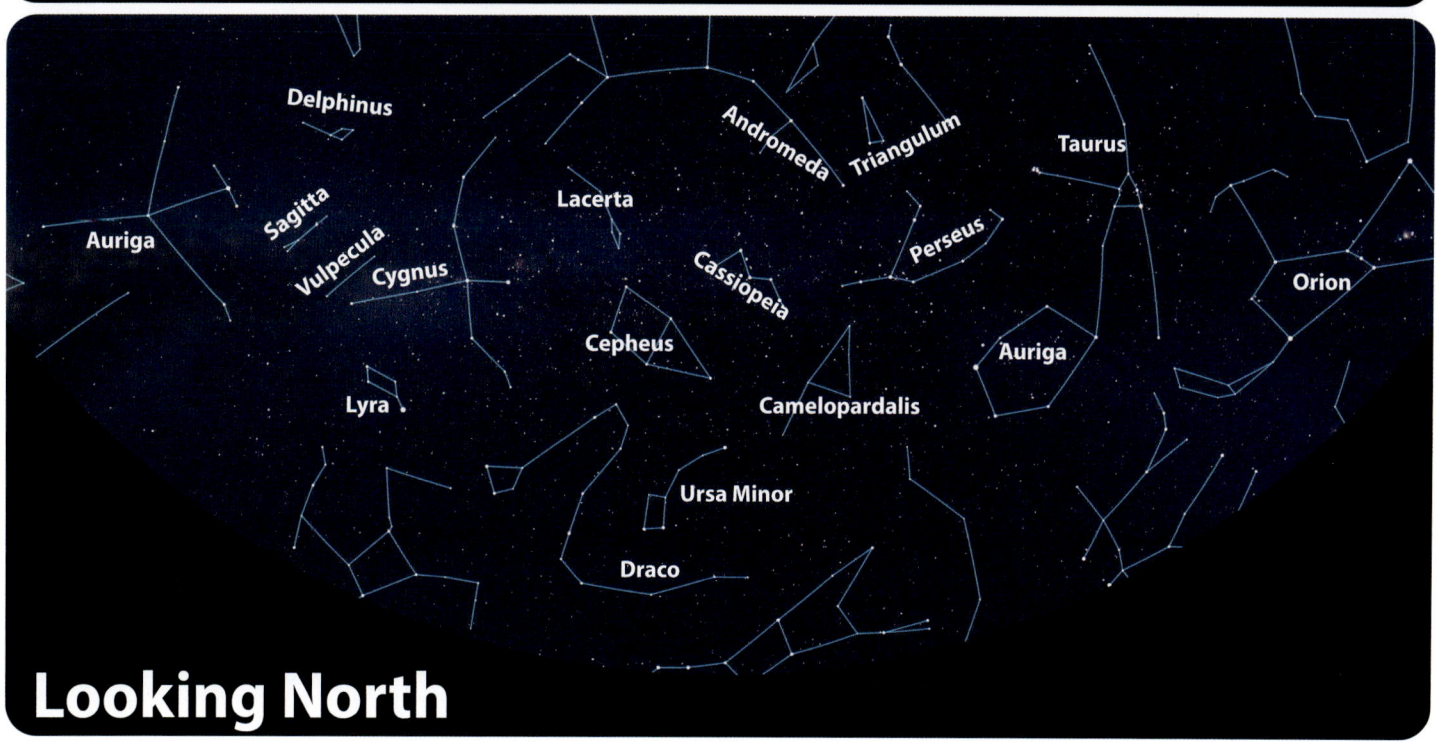

Winter Full-Sky Constellations

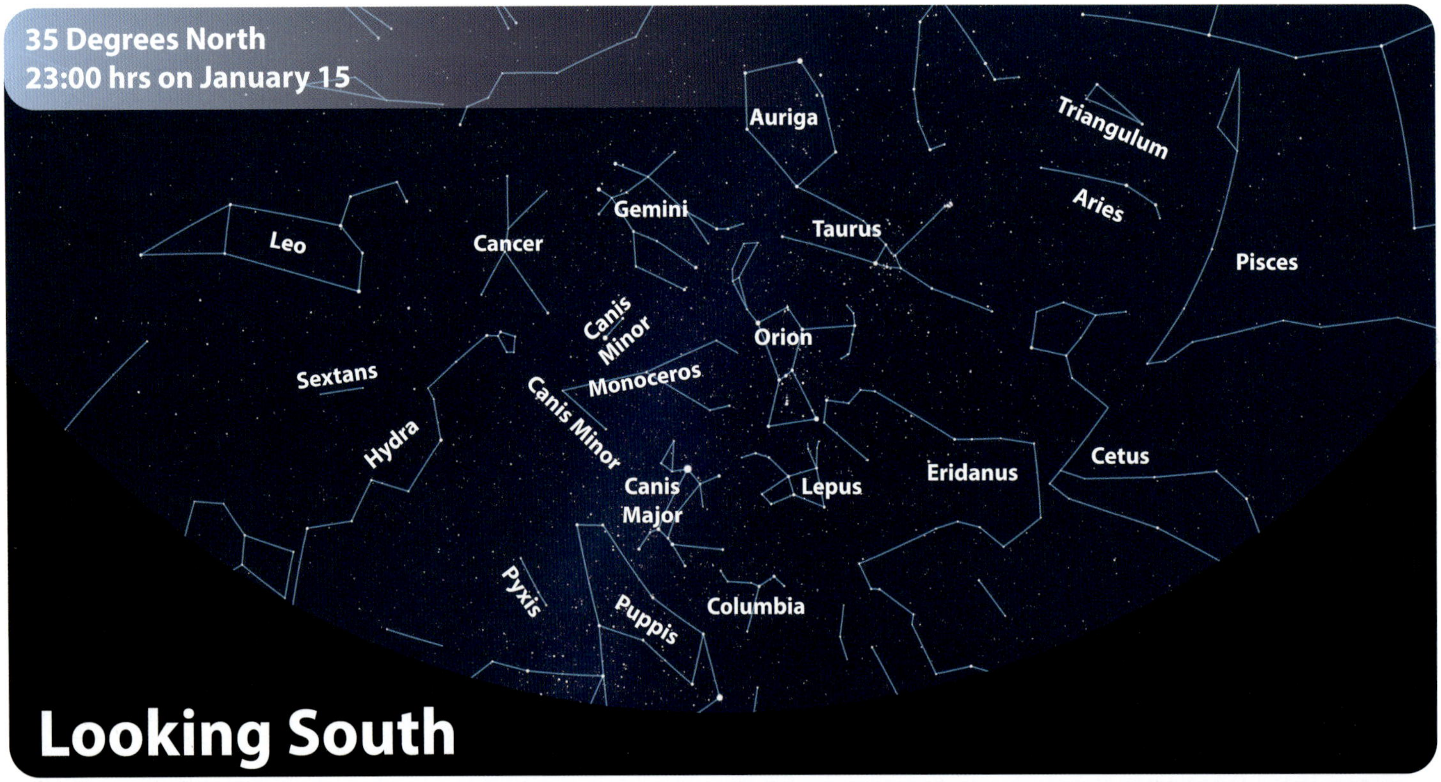

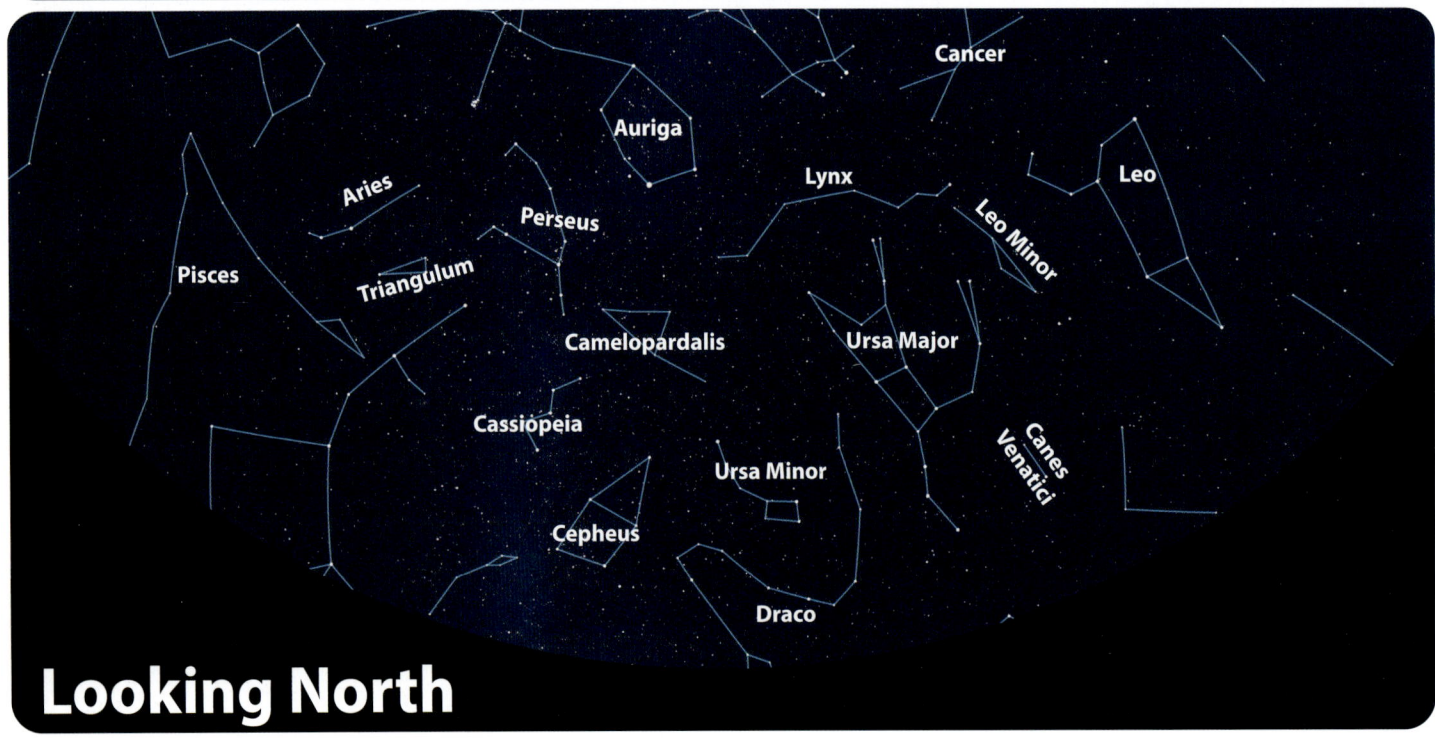

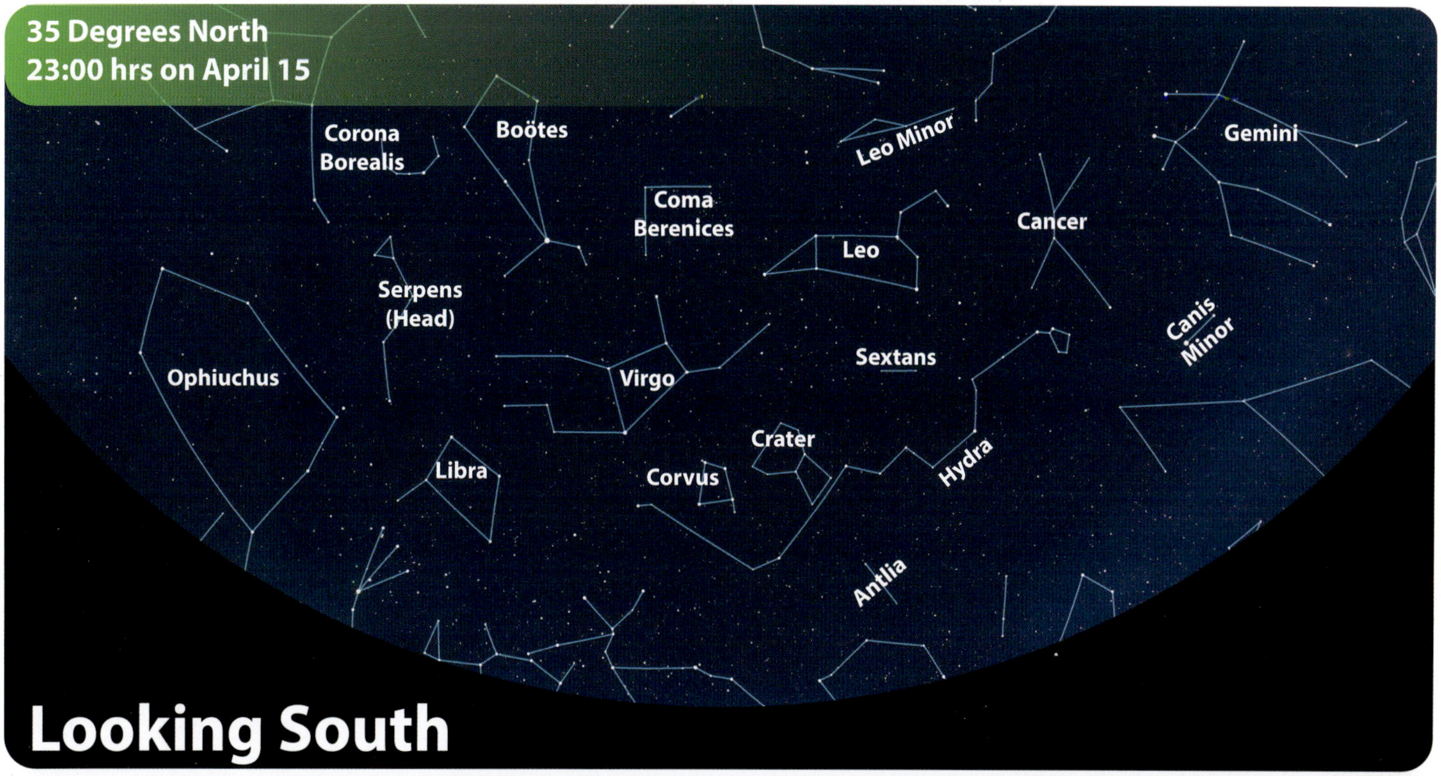

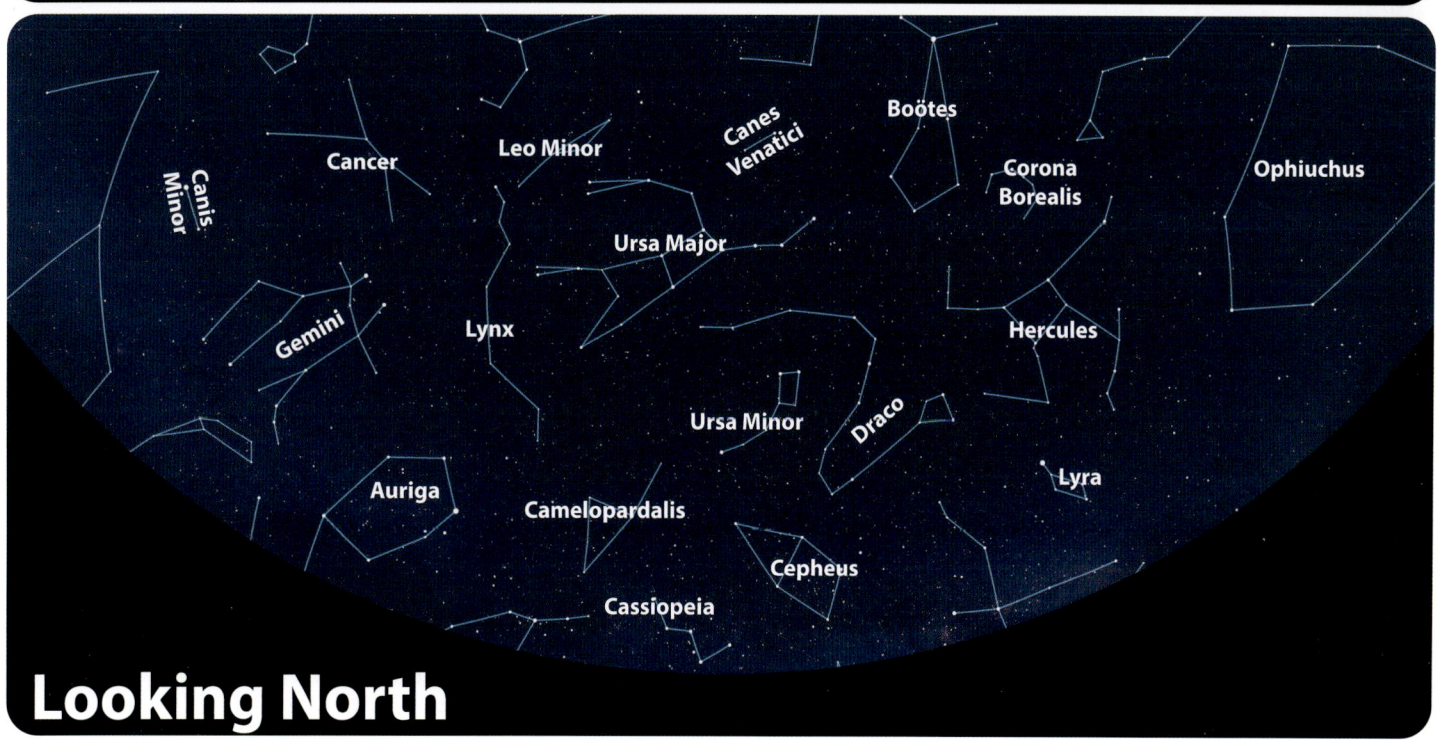

Glossary of Astronomical Terms

Asterism: An unofficial grouping of stars, like a constellation, used to identify patterns in the night sky.

Averted Vision: A technique for looking at deep-sky objects where a dim object brightens when you focus your gaze beside it instead of directly at it.

Conjunction: When two objects, such as the Moon and a planet, meet or pass each other in the sky.

Deep-Sky Object: A stargazing target that resides outside our solar system. This includes galaxies, nebulae, and star clusters.

Diopter: An adjustment to the binoculars to set the focus for vision differences between your eyes. Usually this is accomplished by rotating one of the eyecups.

Ecliptic: The apparent path the Sun takes through the stars throughout the year. The Moon and planets are always found near the ecliptic.

Light-Year: The distance light travels in one year. It is used to measure distances in space. One light-year is about 9,500,000,000,000 kilometers.

Magnitude: A numerical scale that describes the apparent brightness of an object in space as observed from Earth.

Messier List: A list of 110 objects that originated with French comet hunter Charles Messier about 200 years ago.

New General Catalogue (NGC): A list of almost 8,000 nebulae and star clusters compiled in the late 1800s.

Node: The point in the Moon's orbit where it crosses the ecliptic. Eclipses occur when the Moon passes this point during new Moon or full Moon.

Orbit: The curved path an object, such as a planet, moon, or spacecraft, takes as it travels through space.

Opposition: When a planet is directly on the opposite side of the Earth from the Sun.

Sidereal: A period of time measured relative to distant stars.

Sunspot: A magnetic storm on the surface of the Sun that is visible in binoculars or a small telescope.

Waning: Refers to the Moon's phases as it moves from full Moon back to new Moon.

Waxing: Refers to the Moon's phases as it moves from new Moon back to full Moon. These are generally regarded as the best phases to observe the Moon, as it is well positioned in the evening sky.

Appendix

Adding Recent Comets to Stellarium

Comet-finding charts provided by the media usually aren't very intuitive. I've found it easier to make my comet map with Stellarium, but you generally need to add the comet to the software first. To do this, select:

- Configuration>Plugins>Solar System Editor
- Configure>"Solar System">Import orbital Elements in MPC Format
- Select "Comets", select "Gideon van Buitenen: comets", and then click "Get Orbital Elements"
- Search for the comet by name, select it, and click "Add Objects".

Observing Program (Free)

If you have observed most of the objects in this book, and recorded your observations as you went along, it's likely you have met all the requirements for the RASC's Explore the Universe (ETU) Program. See https://www.rasc.ca/explore-universe for the requirements. Note: You do NOT have to be a member of the RASC or live in Canada to apply for your ETU certificate.

OBSERVING LOG

Date: | Time: | Location:

Sky Conditions (Seeing/Transparency):

Instrument (Magnification/Aperture):

Notes:

OBSERVING LOG

Date: | Time: | Location:

Sky Conditions (Seeing/Transparency):

Instrument (Magnification/Aperture):

Notes:

OBSERVING LOG

Date: | Time: | Location:

Sky Conditions (Seeing/Transparency):

Instrument (Magnification/Aperture):

Notes:

OBSERVING LOG

Date: | Time: | Location:

Sky Conditions (Seeing/Transparency):

Instrument (Magnification/Aperture):

Notes:

OBSERVING LOG

Date: Time: Location:

Sky Conditions (Seeing/Transparency):

Instrument (Magnification/Aperture):

Notes:

OBSERVING LOG

Date: Time: Location:

Sky Conditions (Seeing/Transparency):

Instrument (Magnification/Aperture):

Notes:

OBSERVING LOG

Date: Time: Location:

Sky Conditions (Seeing/Transparency):

Instrument (Magnification/Aperture):

Notes:

OBSERVING LOG

Date: Time: Location:

Sky Conditions (Seeing/Transparency):

Instrument (Magnification/Aperture):

Notes:

OBSERVING LOG

| Date: | Time: | Location: |

Sky Conditions (Seeing/Transparency):

Instrument (Magnification/Aperture):

Notes:

OBSERVING LOG

| Date: | Time: | Location: |

Sky Conditions (Seeing/Transparency):

Instrument (Magnification/Aperture):

Notes:

OBSERVING LOG

| Date: | Time: | Location: |

Sky Conditions (Seeing/Transparency):

Instrument (Magnification/Aperture):

Notes:

OBSERVING LOG

| Date: | Time: | Location: |

Sky Conditions (Seeing/Transparency):

Instrument (Magnification/Aperture):

Notes:

OBSERVING LOG

Date: Time: Location:

Sky Conditions (Seeing/Transparency):

Instrument (Magnification/Aperture):

Notes:

OBSERVING LOG

Date: Time: Location:

Sky Conditions (Seeing/Transparency):

Instrument (Magnification/Aperture):

Notes:

OBSERVING LOG

Date: Time: Location:

Sky Conditions (Seeing/Transparency):

Instrument (Magnification/Aperture):

Notes:

OBSERVING LOG

Date: Time: Location:

Sky Conditions (Seeing/Transparency):

Instrument (Magnification/Aperture):

Notes:

OBSERVING LOG

Date: Time: Location:

Sky Conditions (Seeing/Transparency):

Instrument (Magnification/Aperture):

Notes:

OBSERVING LOG

Date: Time: Location:

Sky Conditions (Seeing/Transparency):

Instrument (Magnification/Aperture):

Notes:

OBSERVING LOG

Date: Time: Location:

Sky Conditions (Seeing/Transparency):

Instrument (Magnification/Aperture):

Notes:

OBSERVING LOG

Date: Time: Location:

Sky Conditions (Seeing/Transparency):

Instrument (Magnification/Aperture):

Notes:

OBSERVING LOG

Date:	Time:	Location:

Sky Conditions (Seeing/Transparency):

Instrument (Magnification/Aperture):

Notes:

OBSERVING LOG

Date:	Time:	Location:

Sky Conditions (Seeing/Transparency):

Instrument (Magnification/Aperture):

Notes:

OBSERVING LOG

Date:	Time:	Location:

Sky Conditions (Seeing/Transparency):

Instrument (Magnification/Aperture):

Notes:

OBSERVING LOG

Date:	Time:	Location:

Sky Conditions (Seeing/Transparency):

Instrument (Magnification/Aperture):

Notes:

OBSERVING LOG

Date: Time: Location:

Sky Conditions (Seeing/Transparency):

Instrument (Magnification/Aperture):

Notes:

OBSERVING LOG

Date: Time: Location:

Sky Conditions (Seeing/Transparency):

Instrument (Magnification/Aperture):

Notes:

OBSERVING LOG

Date: Time: Location:

Sky Conditions (Seeing/Transparency):

Instrument (Magnification/Aperture):

Notes:

OBSERVING LOG

Date: Time: Location:

Sky Conditions (Seeing/Transparency):

Instrument (Magnification/Aperture):

Notes:

OBSERVING LOG

Date:　　　　Time:　　　　Location:

Sky Conditions (Seeing/Transparency):

Instrument (Magnification/Aperture):

Notes:

OBSERVING LOG

Date:　　　　Time:　　　　Location:

Sky Conditions (Seeing/Transparency):

Instrument (Magnification/Aperture):

Notes:

OBSERVING LOG

Date:　　　　Time:　　　　Location:

Sky Conditions (Seeing/Transparency):

Instrument (Magnification/Aperture):

Notes:

OBSERVING LOG

Date:　　　　Time:　　　　Location:

Sky Conditions (Seeing/Transparency):

Instrument (Magnification/Aperture):

Notes:

NOTES

NOTES

NOTES

NOTES

NOTES